THE CAPTIVE RABBI

THE
CAPTIVE RABBI

The Story of R. Meir of Rothenburg

by

Lillian S. Freehof

Illustrated by Albert Gold

THE JEWISH PUBLICATION SOCIETY OF AMERICA

5725–1965   PHILADELPHIA

TO
S. B. F.

Mrs. Lillian Freehof, wife of a prominent Pittsburgh rabbi, is the authoress of a number of books for young people, among them *Stories of King David* and *Stories of King Solomon*, both Jewish Publication Society books.

Introductory Note
The Nature of Jewish Heroism

Readers of Covenant Books should welcome the inclusion in the series of the heroic life of Rabbi Meir of Rothenburg. His inclusion, however, may raise the question of the nature of Jewish heroism.

Consider David, King of Israel. When you speak of him as a hero, which events in his life do you have in mind? He slew Goliath and saved his people; he conquered many nations and made them subject to his royal will; he also united the Hebrew tribes in devotion to the God of Israel, and was the author of some of the noblest religious poetry of all time. Which of these activities stamp him as a Jewish hero?

Jewish history has produced both types of hero—the conqueror on the field of battle, like Judah the Maccabee or Simeon Bar-Kokhba; and the leader in religious teaching and inspiration to noble life. The second type has been more numerous during the past two thousand years. His influence has made of the Jewish people primarily a people of scholars and spiritual guides. Every people needs both kinds of hero; but the character of a people can be judged by the type of hero it values most highly.

Introductory Note

Rabbi Meir of Rothenburg was a hero of Jewish spirit. His biography is offered in this book as an example and an inspiration.

The Jewish Publication Society

Contents

Stone walls do not a prison make,
Nor iron bars a cage;
Minds innocent and quiet take
That for an hermitage.

—RICHARD LOVELACE

1

Flames in Paris

THE CITY was Paris. The
year was 1242. The month was June, and the day was
Friday. It was the day of the great bonfire, the burning
of the twenty-four cartloads of the Talmud, the sacred
books which had been cruelly confiscated from the Jews
who lived under the direct authority of King Louis IX
of France.

The red flames shot up into the sky. A roar went up
from the watching crowd. One person in the crowd did
not shout. Young Meir ben Baruch of the city of Worms
on the Rhine, who had come to Paris to study in its
famous *Yeshiva*, watched in silence, barely holding back
his tears.

The huge fire blazed fiercely. Red-hot sparks leaped
towards the heavens as more and more Talmud-scrolls

were added to the flames. But even above the booming roar of the fire, even above the frenzied cries of the onlookers—over all that noise—Meir ben Baruch could hear the maniacal shouting of one man, whom he had been watching.

The man stood on a small platform, as close as he dared come to the fire. He stood straight, with his fists pointed toward the sky, shouting,

"Burn them! Burn them all! To the devil! Throw them to the devil!"

Then, jumping off the platform, he ran to one of the carts, reached in, and grabbed an armful of parchment scrolls. With a cry of triumph, he flung them into the flames. Mounting the platform again, he shouted to the people, urging them to throw more scrolls into the fire. His shrieks were half lost in the howling of the mob, and his face turned redder and redder from his exertions and from the reflection of the flames. In response to his shouting, the massed crowd grew frantic, yelling cries of hate and gloating.

Meir ben Baruch of Worms felt dismally alone in that yelling, milling mob, when suddenly he heard familiar voices. Unexpectedly, he was joined by his two beloved teachers, R. Samuel ben Solomon of Chateau Thierry, and Rabbi Yehiel of Paris. Somehow, they had managed to find him on the outskirts of the mob. They stood next to him, close, as if in their closeness they could shield each other and draw comfort for their pain.

But it was impossible for them to find words with which to ease each other's sorrow. The two old scholars felt it would have been better if they had remained at home, sparing themselves the torture of watching the burning of their sacred books. But their anguish had forced them to come, and now helpless rage kept them rooted to the spot. They knew they would never believe that this fire had really occurred if they did not see it with their own eyes. Even if part of themselves died with the burning books, they knew that it was their sacred duty and their right as human beings to be present.

So all three remained, silent, motionless, as if they had been turned to stone. Only their eyes were alive, eyes that watched in pain every move of the destroyers as the fire rose higher and higher, the flames grew hotter and redder, and the bonfire became a roaring, ravaging furnace. The Paris sky filled with cinders and ashes and flames, and the air was filled with the maddening cries of the maddened crowd.

A fourth man came to join the silent three: Werner of Mayence. He was tall, as tall as Meir, heavier in build and older perhaps by ten years than Meir ben Baruch, who in this fateful year of 1242 was twenty-five years old. Werner stood next to Meir on his right side, not speaking to the three friends. He knew who the two rabbis were, but he did not know Meir.

He kept silent for his own reasons. Now he, too, turned to watch the man on the platform, and on his thin lips there was a tiny smile of contempt.

The flames were crackling now with intense heat, and the people closest to the fire began to move back, pushing against the people behind them. One man, a drunkard, was pushed so hard he fell against Meir ben Baruch, grabbing at the young man's ankle. Meir, without looking at him, thrust him away. The drunkard fell forward on his knees.

He looked up at Meir, started to speak in anger, then became gentle. He muttered, "What's the matter? Why're you cryin', young man, huh, why?"

Meir paid no attention to him, but the drunk persisted, "Should laugh. Everybody's laughing. Why aren't you laughing?"

The drunk looked slyly at Meir, who did not even seem to know he was there. He had eyes only for the red flames, shooting up into the Paris sky, and for the mad man on the platform. The drunk rose unsteadily to his feet, and stood weaving in front of Meir. He bent his knees so as to tilt his head, and peered up into Meir's face.

"Why're you cryin'?" he asked. "Shouldn't cry. Should be happy. See? I'm happy." He threw back his head again and roared with laughter.

The sound was lost in the shouting of the crowd. Meir ignored him. But Werner of Mayence took a step closer to Meir, as if to protect him. The two rabbis on the other side of Meir did not even notice the drunk.

Again, the drunk persisted. "Everybody's happy. Why're you sad? They burning someone you know in that fire? Who're they burning in the fire?"

But Meir had eyes only for the man on the platform silhouetted against the flames.

"Who? Who's in the fire?" The drunk pulled at Meir's sleeve. "Eh? Who're they burning?"

He gave a strong tug on Meir's arm, so that the young man became aware of the drunk, so persistently asking his insane question.

He didn't answer, but the question rang in his mind.

"Who is burning in the fire?"

His eyes remained fixed on the flames shooting upward into the sky of Paris, but in his mind's eye he saw the flames of another fire. That fire had been lighted centuries before, in Palestine, by earlier barbarians who were also impelled by a mad desire to destroy Jewish learning.

"Close your schools!" they had thundered at the scholars and teachers.

And one scholar defied them. Hananiah b. Teradion refused to stop teaching the Torah to his students.

"Cease teaching the Torah!" commanded the barbarians. "Cease! Or you die."

Hananiah b. Teradion scorned their threats of death. He continued to teach the Torah. And he was condemned to death by fire.

So they prepared a huge fire. But it wasn't enough for his persecutors to throw Hananiah onto a flaming pyre and let him perish. They wanted to show their contempt for the Torah for which he was willing to die. They confiscated his Torah scroll and, with curses and obscene oaths, they flung it open, letting it unroll in the dust of the ground. They forced him to stand up straight and they wound the Torah like a wide, long bandage all around his body, trussing his arms and legs. When they had him thus helplessly tied, they propped him up, wrapped in the scroll of the Law, on a pyre of dry brush.

Around Hananiah b. Teradion crowded his pupils, his disciples, struggling to get near him, trying to pull him away from the faggots. But the soliders beat them off with their swords.

The executioner set a torch to the brush. The twigs caught fire and began to crackle and burn, the flame growing brighter and higher until it began to lick at the parchment scroll wound around Hananiah. Now the parchment caught fire and burned rapidly, and the flame reached Hananiah's face. With the first searing touch of the fire on his face, he lifted his eyes skyward and prayed,

"O Lord, forgive me for this Torah which is being destroyed."

The flames leaped towards his eyes, and Hananiah cried, "O Lord, give me strength to die nobly for Thy Holy Name."

And then he beseeched, "O Lord, watch over Thy people Israel. Guard them, O God, from wickedness and danger."

Again his frenzied students struggled to get near him, and again the guards beat them off. Heartbroken and helpless, they wept, and as they wept they pleaded with the martyred rabbi:-

"Master, Master, what do you see?"

And from the depths of the agony of his body and soul, came Rabbi Hananiah's answer.

"The letters of the Law soar upward! The letters of the Law soar upward to God!"

The scene of that ancient fire in Palestine faded from

the mind of Meir. His vision was filled again with the fire burning now, at this very moment, in Paris.

The drunkard again plucked at Meir's sleeve, insisting, insisting, "Who? Who's in the fire? Who are they burning in the fire?"

And now Meir shouted at the drunk. "Whom? Whom are they burning? Whom? You crazy Frenchman! Whom! They're burning you! And me! They're burning the words of God!"

The drunkard turned his head, leaning it on his left shoulder, staring up at the flames.

"God?" he muttered. "They're burning God? I don't see God." He turned his head around, staggered, and fell against Meir, muttering, "Don't see God. Where's God?"

Meir recoiled in disgust. "You fool, you crazy drunk! Go back to the gutter where you belong!" He gave him a violent push. The drunk fell backward and landed in the gutter.

Werner of Mayence moved closer to Meir and said urgently, "Careful. Don't antagonize anyone. Careful!"

Meir turned in bewilderment at the friendly voice. The stranger smiled at him. Shaking his head gently, Werner repeated, "Careful, my friend."

On Meir's other side, R. Samuel b. Solomon tugged at his sleeve. "Meir, come away. Come away before you get into trouble."

"No, I must stay. I must stay until the last scroll is burned in their cruel fire."

Then words seemed to form in his mind. They ar-

ranged themselves in lines, and he began to whisper his
hymn to the burning books:-

> Ask, is it well, O thou consumed of fire,
> With those that mourn for thee,
> That yearn to tread thy courts, that sore
> desire Thy sanctuary.*

If Meir ben Baruch had taken the trouble to tell the
annoying drunkard that this stupid Parisian mob was
burning cartload upon cartload of books, the drunk
would have laughed and said, "Books? You weep over
books?"

Yes, thought Meir, I weep over books. But not just
ordinary books. I weep for the Talmud, the most holy
book next to the Bible.

"But if you still have the Bible," the drunk might have
insisted, "why do you care if you lose the Talmud?"

Why do I care if I lose the Talmud?

Meir ben Baruch shook his head forlornly. But suddenly he pulled his body up stiffly, and the men on either
side of him turned to see what had alerted him. It was
the man on the platform. He had turned slowly around,
surveying the crowd, his face distorted with an unholy
joy. Then, unbelievably, out of that whole mob of excited, frenzied people, his half-crazed eyes picked out R.
Yehiel. The joy on his face changed to violent hatred.
He raised his fists to the sky and shouted out over the
mob at the Rabbi, and his voice reached the ears of the
four watching men over the deafening tumult.

* From "The Burning of the Law," written by R. Meir of Rothenburg.

He shrieked, "I did it! I did it!"

Suddenly he jumped down from the platform and began pushing his way through the crowd to R. Yehiel. It took him many minutes to fight his way through the milling, dangerous mob. By the time he reached the four men, Meir ben Baruch was standing in front of R. Yehiel. Close to R. Yehiel on the left stood R. Solomon, and close to him on the right stood Werner of Mayence.

The man stopped in front of Meir. His hair was singed from the fire. Smoke and soot had blackened his face in streaks. His face was twisted with hatred, and his eyes burned as murderously as the fire at his back.

"Nicholas Donin," Meir ben Baruch said softly, but with such scorn in his voice that another man might have quailed.

But Nicholas Donin sneered. "Step aside, you," he ordered. "I would speak to that most saintly of saints, Rabbi Yehiel." He spat out the words.

"You have nothing to say to Rabbi Yehiel," Meir said quietly. "He has nothing to say to you."

Nicholas Donin threw back his head and laughed harshly. "You are right, you young rooster, whoever you are. I've said everything to Rabbi Yehiel I need to say."

He half turned and flung his arm out towards the roaring fire. "There's all I have to say, Rabbi. There it is." He laughed raucously. "There are your precious Talmuds!"

He turned back now to the men, the laughter gone, the insane light back in his eyes. His face was contorted into a mask of such hatred that Meir put up his arm to protect Rabbi Yehiel. Nicholas Donin's voice was no longer hoarse, no longer screeching. It was cold now, cold as ice, and deadly, as deadly as the raging fire at his back.

"I have won," he said. "I have won."

The flames of the fire shot heavenward.

2

I Would Defend the Right . . .

"**W**HO IS THIS Nicholas Donin?"

That was the question Meir ben Baruch had asked when he came to Paris two years before. And now, two years later, he had the complete answer. Nicholas Donin was a traitor to the Jews.

This traitor had done as much harm to his fellow-Jews as one man could do. Having flung the taunt of his treachery into the face of his former teacher, Rabbi Yehiel, he shouted it once more, his voice yelling obscenely over the roar of the fire and the shouting of the hate-inflamed mob.

"I have won! *I have won! I HAVE WON!*"

He looked coldly and gloatingly at each of the four men, then turned on his heel and began pushing his way back through the mob. They stood silently watching him, losing sight of him for a few moments in the throng, then catching a glimpse of him again as he threaded his way through the crowd. Until, once more, he leaped up to the platform and took up his triumphant stance, emblazoned by the roaring flames.

Suddenly, Rabbi Samuel ben Solomon drooped. His head sagged, his shoulders slumped, and the life seemed to flow out of his face as he turned his haggard eyes to his companions.

"He has won. We must go now, Yehiel. Nicholas Donin has won."

"Oh no!" Meir ben Baruch shouted. Then, in a more normal tone: "What has he won? The burning up of a few Talmud-books? There are more, hundreds more. The flame of knowledge burning in the Talmud will never be extinguished. Let him light up the skies of Paris with a few parchments. Our Talmud still lives!"

R. Solomon smiled wanly. "You see, Yehiel? It is only the old who get discouraged. The young find strength to go on." He straightened his shoulders, raised his head, and smiled at his brilliant student from Germany. "Well said, Meir. Take heart from your own words. Keep heart. You will never falter. You have the courage and the strength to keep going."

But his words, and Meir's, had no effect in cheering R. Yehiel. He looked at his companions with dull eyes, and without speaking, turned to leave.

"You will come with us, Meir?" R. Solomon asked, turning to leave with his friend.

"No, no," Meir said impatiently. "Do not wait for me. I will stay a while."

"Take care, Meir," R. Solomon said gently. "Take care."

Meir watched his two teachers walk slowly and sadly away from the tragic bonfire, and his face was stern. Werner of Mayence, who had kept silent except for his cautious warning during the episode with the drunkard, spoke now.

"Perhaps Rabbi Solomon is right," he said quietly. "The mob is dangerous tonight, and you, if I may presume, are too bold. May I suggest that you walk off with me, and we may talk perhaps, and if you wish, have a bit of supper at my house?"

Meir ben Baruch turned in surprise. The stranger smiled.

"My name is Werner," he said, "and I come from Mayence . . ."

"Oh. Then perhaps you know my uncle . . ." Meir ben Baruch gave a twisted smile. The stranger was not a Jew; he was clearly a Christian. How could he know Meir's uncle? He turned brooding eyes back to the fire and said, half apologetically, "No, I believe you would not know my uncle."

"What is his name?" Werner asked.

"He is the Rabbi of Mayence . . ."

"Rabbi Judah ben Moses Ha-Kohen?" Werner interrupted. "Indeed, I do know him. Then you are his nephew Meir. I have heard him speak often of you and your brother Abraham."

Meir turned back to the stranger, half smiling. "Yes, I am Meir."

Ah, so this is Meir, thought Werner, the genius, the brilliant nephew who has outstripped his brilliant father and uncles. It was a family of fine scholars, Werner knew, and this young man was considered the genius of the family. Meir's uncle had expressed his surprise to Werner just the year before that his nephew had gone to Paris for further study with R. Yehiel and R. Samuel b. Solomon.

Talking lightly of Meir's uncle and of Mayence, Werner skillfully led Meir away from the bonfire, without the young man realizing the adroit maneuver. He asked Meir questions so casually, so artlessly, that Meir found himself telling Werner a great deal about himself.

Yes, he was married; his wife Sarah was beautiful and black-haired. He had children, two lovely little daughters, Rebecca and Deborah. The separation from his family was difficult, but it was only here, in Paris, that he could study with R. Samuel b. Solomon and R. Yehiel.

Before long they were sitting comfortably in Werner's garden. The stillness and quiet were so far removed from the noise and the shouting of the bonfire just a few squares away that Meir might have imagined it had all been an evil nightmare, except that he could still smell the smoke of the fire. And there, in the quiet rose-garden, Werner asked a question which had bothered Meir for some time.

"I noticed that you seemed angry even with Rabbi Yehiel? Why?"

Meir looked up sharply. "Why should you think I am angry with my teacher?"

Werner did not answer. He just smiled, slightly, and cut a grape from the bunch on his plate. Anger flamed quickly and brightly in Meir, and he needed the relief of expressing it.

"I would defend the right . . ."

Then, ashamed, grief-stricken at almost speaking out against his teacher, he stopped abruptly.

Werner made no response, merely cut off another grape, and turned his eyes toward the center of town where the smoke of the bonfire was still visible. Sparks were still shooting up into the sky. Meir followed his gaze, and the shooting sparks rekindled his desire to rid his mind of his obsession. There was no one in whom he could confide because he could complain of his teacher to no one, if a complaint was what he had against him. But this man was a stranger. He would never see him again. Still, loyalty sealed his lips.

He spoke, but guardedly. "I would defend the right of any man to his beliefs, to his opinions . . . and so I would defend the right of Nicholas Donin to express his differences with his own community, with his fellow-Jews. But Nicholas Donin has brought punishment upon his fellow-Jews in order to satisfy his own hurt feelings. That I can never forgive."

Werner pushed the dishes away from him. He wiped his fingers and his mouth with his napkin, and pushed his chair away from the table. He leaned toward Meir, speaking quietly, firmly, "I was present at the court trial, Rabbi Meir. I heard how ardently Rabbi Yehiel de-

fended the Talmud against the charges which Nicholas
Donin brought."

"Then tell me about it," Meir said tensely. "Rabbi
Yehiel will not talk about the trial. So I know nothing. I
must know . . . I cannot rest without knowing what
happened at the trial . . ."

He paused, again fearful that his words would show
disloyalty to his teacher.

"You know the beginning," Werner said. "I know the
end. I will tell you the end, if you will tell me the beginning. Why are you angry with Rabbi Yehiel?"

Meir ben Baruch of Worms looked at Werner of
Mayence . . . Werner who? Werner what? Who was
Werner? Dare he talk to him? Meir was not asking himself these questions for the first time. He had wondered
about his companion ever since they had walked away
from the bonfire together. He knew Werner to be a
Christian, but perhaps not necessarily an enemy of the
Jews. He thought he could read in the other man's face
honesty, integrity, decency. These estimates seemed
strengthened by everything Werner had said or done in
the past hour. When he finally decided to talk, unknown
to himself that day and for many a year, Meir performed
a great service for the Jews.

"Nicholas Donin. Who is Nicholas Donin? Before I
speak of him, let me tell you first what the Talmud is.
The Talmud is our most important possession. It is our
fortress. It is our strength. Need I tell you of the dangers
in this age for my people?"

Werner had already shown himself to be a man of

intelligence, knowledge, and insight. It was not necessary to inform him of the great changes which were occurring in the political, economic and cultural life of Europe.

The barbarian hordes had swept over Europe, leaving ruin behind them. Three great religious crusades had sapped the strength and the financial resources of the countries of Europe. The feudal system was giving way to a new economic structure.

Trade was starting up. The cities on the sea-coasts were finding a new power in sea-trade. And the merchants of the towns, the burghers, were beginning to occupy an increasingly important place.

"And out of this new order in Europe," Werner said into the silence, "everybody is trying to pull the biggest plum for himself. The king wants power, the burgher wants order, and the religious groups want complete dominance."

"With the Jew squeezed by them all," Meir said tightly. "Everyone is trying to bleed him white. And he has only one security . . . his learning . . . his Talmud."

"Political asylum also," Werner said in a murmur. "The Jews have been granted the right to live in Germany and in France."

"If they can live as Jews," Meir said as quietly. "They've been willing to pay large sums of money for the privilege of settling here and in Germany. They are willing to pay, and you know they do pay, Werner . . ."

Werner nodded. And Meir went on.

"They pay, they pay . . . but they must live as Jews.

They will not give up their personal freedoms. And their personal freedoms are included in their own laws of justice and in their own codes of law, laws and codes which are derived from the Talmud."

"The kings and the princes of Germany and France have been willing to permit the Jews to live as a separate group," Werner said. "They are permitted to follow their own customs and live within their own laws . . ."

"Providing," Meir smiled, "ah, providing they *do* pay, and pay heavily for these privileges. But we are willing. It has been agreed, and it is satisfactory to both sides. You know the taxes are exorbitant . . ."

Werner nodded again, sighing shallowly.

"But the Jews pay these exorbitant taxes," Meir said, "and the kings leave them to their own self-government. And the Jew is able to live according to the laws of the Talmud."

The Talmud, Meir explained, was for the Jew the highest authority in law and religion, in custom and ritual, in group organization and business activities. It was the life of the Jew. With his Talmud he could be a self-respecting child of God, seeking justice for all and mercy to all.

With his Talmud he could live as a Jew.

Without his Talmud he could not live.

And now the barbarians of Paris were burning the Talmud!

Overcome by sudden emotion, Meir jumped up from his chair, unable to contain himself. His body burned hotly, as if he himself had been thrown into those flames along with the Talmud. Then he quieted down, and turned again to Werner.

"All because of one traitorous Jew, Nicholas Donin. What turns a man into a traitor, Werner?"

Werner shrugged slightly. "Fear. Guilty conscience. But what put him on the road to treachery?"

Then Meir told the story:-

Nicholas Donin was a native of LaRochelle, France. In his youth he had been a Talmud scholar. But after a while he rejected the talmudic interpretation of the Bible, and said that *only* the Bible was the true source of God's inspiration, and the Talmud was untrue. He decided that the Talmud must be discarded and that the Jews must live only by the laws of the Bible.

The rabbis knew that Donin's attitude was a threat to their people and their way of life. They pleaded with him to change his views, and tried to show him where he erred. They tried to convince him of the value of the Talmud in the life of the Jew.

But Donin, convinced that he was right, scorned them and mocked their teachings. The quarrel became more bitter and intense until finally, he was threatened with excommunication.

Excommunication was no small punishment. It involved being expelled from the community, and, at a time when the power of a curse was feared, it included the curse of the entire community.

But Donin, though threatened with excommunication, continued to defy his teachers. The Talmud, he said, was nothing. The Talmud must be destroyed.

Donin was excommunicated. It was Rabbi Yehiel who had issued the decree of excommunication.

"He told me why he did it," Meir said to Werner. " 'I excommunicated Donin,' he said, 'because there was no truth in his mouth, faith had been cut out from his heart, and he had become a root producing gall and wormwood.' "

"Was it a stern punishment?" Werner asked.

Meir nodded soberly. "Yes, it was. I believe every man has the right to decide how he will live, and I would defend that right . . . But there would be chaos in the community if each person took the law into his own hands. The law is made to bring order to the community, and if a man chooses to live within a certain community, he must abide by its rules."

"Then surely Rabbi Yehiel had a right to excommunicate Donin?"

Meir sighed. "Perhaps. But the Rabbi had observed Donin for a long time. He knew what a dangerous person he was. Perhaps he should have tried harder to make him understand the need of the Jewish community to be governed by the Talmud. But perhaps Rabbi Yehiel was too impatient . . . and Donin was excommunicated . . ."

"Then what happened?" Werner asked.

Meir pointed to the flames still shooting up into the sky of Paris.

"Donin, in his fury, sought revenge."

3

Scene at Court

DONIN became a Christian.
In his hatred of all Jewish communities, Nicholas Donin sought the most bitter revenge he could find. Everything he said from that time on about the Jews was a slander.

He started false rumors, claiming the Jews were murderers. He accused them of the murder of an innocent Christian, saying the slain man's blood was to be used during the Passover services. This false rumor caused the death, without trial, of many innocent Jews; death after torture.

He gained admission to the court of the Emperor Frederick II, and told him that the Talmud contained insults directed against Christianity. When the Emperor did not take him seriously enough, Nicholas went to

Pope Gregory IX and brought his charges against the Talmud.

"The Talmud, Your Holiness," said Nicholas, "distorts the words of Holy Writ. It contains disgraceful representations of God Himself. The Talmud is held in higher esteem by the rabbis than the Bible, and is filled with abuse against the founder of the Christian faith. It is the Talmud, Your Holiness, which prevents the Jews from accepting Christianity. Without the Talmud, certainly they would give up their stubborn unbelief. Let the Talmud be taken away from them and they will all become Christians."

The Pope listened intently.

Nicholas Donin continued. "In the Talmud, Your Holiness, it states boldly that it is permissible for a Jew to deal dishonestly with a Christian."

"No!" exclaimed the Pope.

"Yes," insisted Nicholas. "And it further says in the Talmud that it is a worthy thing to kill Christians!"

"Nicholas," asked the Pope sternly, "are you telling the truth?"

Donin nodded gravely, seriously. "Indeed, Your Holiness. In the Talmud of the Jews it is written that if a Christian rests on the Sabbath or studies the Law of the Jews, he is to be punished by death. Oh, it is full of wickedness. Jews may break their oath, particularly if they are dealing with Christians, and they may deceive a Christian whenever they wish. Ah yes, it shows the Jews to be what they really are, dishonest, deceitful, haters of Christians and haters even of God!"

The Pope rose, towering over Nicholas Donin. In a harsh, bitter voice, he said,

"Very well. I shall destroy the Talmud! I shall send orders to the heads of the Church in France, in England, Castile, Aragon and Portugal. I shall have them confiscate all copies! The task shall be completed by the morning of the first Saturday of Lent. The confiscated Talmuds shall be given over to the monks, to the Dominicans and the Franciscans, who shall subject the Talmud to a careful examination. If your charges, Nicholas, prove correct, the Talmuds shall be burned!"

Then the Pope gave Nicholas a special letter.

"Deliver this to William, the Bishop of Paris," he ordered. "My letter charges him to search out every Talmud in the city of Paris, and to burn every one."

Once dismissed from the Pope's presence, Nicholas sang aloud with joy. Now he was getting his revenge. The Jews would be more than sorry they had excommunicated him. He would show them with whom they were dealing!

He left immediately for Paris, where he handed over the Pope's letter to William, the Bishop of Paris. The Bishop, quite eager to carry out the Pope's orders, had no trouble convincing the King, Louis IX, to agree to the examination and the burning of the Talmuds.

On the advice of the Bishop of Paris, the King ordered every Jew, under penalty of death, to surrender his Talmud. Thus the Talmud was to be put on trial.

It seemed a peculiar thing, to put a book on trial, as if it were a criminal. How could a book be tried in a court of law? The King, however, worked out a way to conduct a trial in which the Talmud stood in the dock as the accused.

Four rabbis were ordered to hold a public debate with Nicholas Donin on the merits of the Talmud. Nicholas, as prosecuting attorney, would present the charges against the book. If the rabbis could prove them false, the Talmud would be safe. But if Nicholas won the case, the books were to be burned.

At least the rabbis were given a chance to defend their sacred book.

The King, to make it appear that the trial was to be an honest one, permitted the Jewish community to choose its own rabbis for the debate.

The community chose four rabbis: Yehiel of Paris, Moses of Couçy, Jehuda ben David of Melun, and Samuel ben Solomon of Chateau Thierry. Each one was to be examined separately and to give their answers to their accuser, Nicholas Donin. Rabbi Yehiel was chosen to undergo the examination first.

"This is as far as I know the story," Meir said to Werner, "except that on the morning of June the 25th, two years ago, five of Rabbi Yehiel's students and friends, and I amongst them, went with him to the palace of the King. We were stopped at the gates, and only Rabbi Yehiel was permitted to enter. But you were there. You know what happened. Tell me."

It was Werner's turn to talk.

Many people were present in the great hall of the palace that day—the bishops of Paris and Senlis, a dozen Dominican monks, the court scribes, the guards of the court . . . and Nicholas Donin. The King was on his throne, attired in his robes of state. On a smaller throne at his right sat the Queen-Mother Blanche. Rabbi Yehiel was ushered into the room.

Little time was wasted in social courtesies. It was made known to the King that this was the Jew, Rabbi Yehiel, who would engage in a disputation with Nicholas Donin of LaRochelle.

Donin began by proclaiming these lies:-

"Is it not true, Rabbi (and his voice dripped with scorn over the word 'Rabbi'), that the Talmud contains miserable abuse against Christianity? Is it not true, Rabbi, that the Talmud contains blasphemy against God?"

Rabbi Yehiel cast a look of contempt upon the erstwhile Jew, turned his back on him, and bowed his head slightly to the King and the Queen-Mother.

"Your Majesties," he said quietly. "You must grant me permission to refuse to answer these rude questions. We Jews are in possession of the constitution issued by the popes which assures our independence in our personal lives. The Talmud which is being questioned here today, Your Majesties, the Talmud is the very essence of the life of the Jew. For the Talmud I am prepared to die. For the Talmud every Jew is prepared to die."

The good Queen-Mother Blanche cried out, "No, no, Rabbi Yehiel. No one's life is in danger. Believe me, Rabbi, your lives are safe. I shall protect you."

"She was sincere," Werner of Mayence said softly. "Rabbi Yehiel's life had never been in danger."

Only the life of the Talmud was threatened. No one

albert gold

placed a hand on the Rabbi or treated him roughly. But lies had been hurled at him, lies which he was supposed to admit as truth.

When the Queen-Mother promised to protect him, Rabbi Yehiel bowed to her. "God will reward your mercy. But, alas, Your Majesty, while you promise to protect the life of the Jew, you are ready to destroy the life of his religion, the sacred Talmud."

"No one talks of destroying anything," the Queen-Mother answered. But she wet her lips nervously.

Rabbi Yehiel's heart sank.

The Queen-Mother continued, "All we ask of you now, honored sage, is to answer the questions."

"He must take an oath," shouted Nicholas Donin. "Without an oath he will pervert the truth. He will weave subtleties around it . . . and evasions! We want the truth! He must take an oath!"

The King leaned forward on his throne. "Surely that is a simple enough matter."

But Rabbi Yehiel shook his head. "Your Majesty," he said quietly. "I must refuse to take an oath. Never in my life have I taken one. I will not invoke the name of God in vain."

"Rabbi Yehiel need take no oath," pronounced the Queen-Mother.

And the Court, sullenly, accepted her decision.

"Now, now," cried out the Bishop of Paris. "Let us get on with the questions. Nicholas, state your first charge."

Nicholas Donin drew himself up to his full height. His

lip curled with hatred, he shouted out the first accusation.

"In the Talmud there are insulting remarks about God."

Rabbi Yehiel sighed shallowly, and then said quietly, "Your Majesties, the whole life of the Jew is wrapped up in his love and devotion of God. It is unthinkable that any self-respecting Jew could utter anything but the highest praise of God. Indeed, I state firmly that the allegation is a lie."

"You dare say I lie!" shouted Nicholas. "Then what about the founder of Christianity? Deny that if you can! Deny that in the Talmud there are insulting remarks about Jesus! Deny it! Deny it!"

Rabbi Yehiel's face turned white, but his voice remained steady.

"Your Majesties, no reference is made to Jesus of Nazareth. If there are certain offensive statements in the Talmud concerning a certain Jeshua or Jesus, those statements refer to the son of Pantheras. His name was Jesus also. Indeed, Your Majesties, the Father of the Church, Hieronymus, and other Church Fathers were acquainted with the Talmud, and they have never said that it contained sentiments hostile to the Christian faith. Nicholas, this Nicholas Donin, is the first person to make such an accusation."

Hour after hour the examination went on. And hour after hour Rabbi Yehiel stood courageously in the court of Louis IX refuting every charge, denying every accusation.

The shadows of twilight fell, and the court was dismissed for the day. But Yehiel was not permitted to leave the palace.

On the second day, Rabbi Yehiel was brought back into the court, and again he was questioned hour after hour by Nicholas Donin. And he refuted every charge. He clung stubbornly to his proud assertion that only truth and justice were contained in the Talmud.

And the second day drew to a close.

Rabbi Yehiel's examination ended on the second day, but he was not permitted to leave the palace until Rabbi Judah of Melun was examined.

"As you know," Werner concluded his account of the trial, "Rabbi Judah of Melun gave exactly the same answers which Rabbi Yehiel had given. And then it was over. The King decided not to question the other two rabbis. Nicholas Donin's lies won . . . and the Talmud was condemned."

Then Werner repeated the statement given out by the Examining Commission:-

THE TWO RABBIS WHO HAVE BEEN EXAMINED, RABBI YEHIEL OF PARIS, AND JUDAH OF MELUN, HAVE BEEN COMPELLED TO ADMIT THE TRUTH OF SEVERAL OF THE CHARGES BROUGHT AGAINST THE TALMUD.
IT IS THE EXPRESS ORDER OF THE KING THAT EVERY TALMUD IN THE CITY OF PARIS BE BURNED.

"Lies, all lies," Meir ben Baruch muttered between clenched teeth. "Why, Werner, why?" he asked. "Why is the lie believed?"

"People believe what they want to believe, Meir," Werner said softly.

Meir nodded absently. "And then from despair we were thrown into jubilation. An unexpected friend appeared."

"The Archbishop Walter Cornutus," Werner nodded gloomily.

The Archbishop Walter Cornutus of Sens, who had great influence with the King, interceded. He persuaded the King not to burn the Talmuds, and the Jews were jubilant. But their joy was short-lived, for suddenly, without warning, the Archbishop was struck down by death.

The Dominican monks, a fanatical and intolerant order, went triumphantly to the King to persuade him that the Archbishop's death was an ill omen. "Do you see what befell the Archbishop when he tried to save the wicked Talmud?" they said. "He was struck dead! Dead! Save yourself from death, O King. Order the Talmuds to be burned!"

Louis IX ordered the Talmuds to be burned.

"And now," Werner concluded, "I suppose you believe it is all Rabbi Yehiel's fault for having excommunicated Donin!"

"I did think so," Meir said. "I argued with him about having excommunicated Donin. But I suppose that no one could have known that Donin would go so far in his attempts for revenge. No, I no longer blame my teacher. I blame the tortuous twistings of a mind like Donin's that feeds on the destruction of his own brothers."

There was silence for a moment, and then Werner said softly,

"You know, Meir, that once Donin had proclaimed his lies, no words that Rabbi Yehiel might have spoken, neither his words nor the words of anyone else, could possibly have avoided this crime. The King and his court came together in a dumb show—it was only a travesty of justice. You know that."

Meir nodded gloomily. "Yes, I know. If the Jews had come bearing golden words directly from Mount Sinai, it would not have mattered. The verdict was pronounced long before the trial. The result was a foregone conclusion. Neither Rabbi Yehiel's words, nor the words of Moses had he come back to earth, would have made any difference at all."

Werner nodded. "The Talmuds were doomed to the flames long before the trial."

"Then why the farce of the trial?" Meir ben Baruch ground out. "Why the stupid performance?"

Werner shrugged lightly. "To ease their own consciences. The King likes to sleep at night. Now he can sleep with a clear conscience because he can say to anyone, to his mother, the Queen, to his court, to the Pope, even to God Himself: 'My hands are clean. I gave the Jews their chance to defend the Talmud.' "

Werner's voice faded away. Meir had nothing more to say. He rose to leave. On that night in June in the year 1242, when Meir ben Baruch of Worms said goodbye to Werner of Mayence, the two men did not know if they would ever meet again.

The Captive Rabbi

Meir walked away from the quiet garden, back to the center of Paris. But he could not return to his rooms. The grief had not yet gone out of his mind; the feeling of bitterness was not yet wiped away from his heart. And so he wandered.

He wandered all night long searching for comfort and relief from his sorrow. And as he walked through the darkened streets, lighted only by the flickering stars, lines of poetry which eased his spirit came to his mind. Into the black Parisian night he whispered:-

> Ask, is it well, O thou consumed of fire!
> Lo, I will weep for thee until my tears
>   Swell as a stream and flow
> Unto the graves where thy two princely seers
>   Sleep calm below:
>
> Moses; and Aaron in the Mountain Hor;
>   I will of them inquire:
> Is there another to replace this Law
>   Devoured of fire?*

---

* From "The Burning of the Law," written by R. Meir of Rothenburg, translated by Nina Davis, in *Songs of Exile*, p. 83.

4

The Call to Rothenburg

Two MEN had decided the
direction of Rabbi Meir's life. One was Nicholas Donin,
the Jew turned Christian who tried to destroy the Jews
by slander. The other man was the political master of
Central Europe, Rudolph, the Emperor of Germany.
The Emperor's aim was different from Donin's. He did
not want to destroy the Jews—he merely wanted to enslave them.

From the beginning of their lives, R. Meir and
Rudolph the First were destined to struggle against each
other.

Meir was born in Worms, Germany, in 1215. Rudolph was born in Limburg, Germany, in 1218. Meir
was born into a family of wealth, great scholarship, and
influence, while Rudolph was born into the ruling fam-

ily. He was born a prince; he would die an Emperor. Meir was a Jew, Rudolph a Christian. Rudolph would strive for domination over the Jews. Meir would shield his people from Rudolph's rapacity.

But that was still in the future. Now it was 1245 and Meir was still in Paris, studying with his famous teachers. Suddenly he felt that he had had enough of Paris, of France, of study, and of separation from his family. It was time to return home.

Three years had passed since the burning of the Talmuds. The first event had been followed by a second burning in 1244. This second episode had increased Meir ben Baruch's impatience to return home, to leave France. Life in Germany certainly was not perfect, but it was better than in France.

By now his yearning to be with his family was so great that nothing else mattered. It had been difficult to be away from them for so long, his wife, Sarah, and his two daughters, Rebecca and Deborah. Once each year he had been able to return home to Worms for a short while, and at least he had seen his children then. But he had missed the joy of watching them grow from babies into little girls.

However, he had had to make a sacrifice—to sacrifice either the opportunity to study with two great masters, Rabbi Yehiel, and Rabbi Samuel b. Solomon, or to sacrifice being with his family. Life was made up of these choices, he knew, and after having made a decision, there was no use regretting it. He had greatly benefited from these five inspiring years of study with two great teachers. Now he was ready to leave them and to return to his family.

So Meir was going home, that is, he was going back to Germany, but not to remain in Worms. He was going to Rothenburg to begin his active career.

The Jewish community of Rothenburg had invited him to become its rabbi. Before he could accept the offer, however, he had to obtain permission to live in Rothenburg. It was not possible for a Jew to settle in any city in Germany without formal permission from the government.

Meir had sent his application, with his signature in Hebrew, as was required, to the city council of Rothenburg. Eventually he had received his official permit, stamped with the municipal seal, granting him the right to settle in Rothenburg. He turned his back on Paris, and his face and his footsteps towards his new home and future in Rothenburg.

The medieval walled city of Rothenburg, located on the river Tauber, in Middle Franconia, Germany, became the home of Meir ben Baruch. From the moment of his arrival he was known to the Jewish world as Rabbi Meir of Rothenburg.

Rothenburg was not a new settlement for the Jews of the Middle Ages. They had come there as early as the beginning of the twelfth century. When Meir came to serve as their rabbi, the Jews had been settled there for over a hundred years.

In July of 1245, R. Meir, traveling from Paris, and his family, traveling from Worms, were reunited in Rothenburg. His two daughters greeted him in their character-istic fashion. Rebecca, the older child, now nine years old, came running with her black curls flying, her arms outstretched, and her joyous cry of "Father, Father" shouted out for the world to hear. Deborah, two years younger, was a sedate little miss at seven, and although her joy at seeing her father was as great as her sister's, she expressed it only with deep smiles; but her little arms hugged Meir fiercely.

The family settled rapidly in a large stone house. The girls were delighted with it. It was extremely large (there were twenty-one rooms) and there was room enough for all sorts of games—for hide and seek on rainy days, a courtyard to play in, and a garden which would bloom as soon as their mother could put her green thumb to work.

For the children, the large house meant room to play. For Sarah, it meant hard work and constant supervision of her staff to keep it clean and wholesome and cheerful. For R. Meir, it meant sufficient space to house the students who would come to the college he planned to establish.

Each member of the family went about the task of making the new habitation their home, in his or her own fashion. Deborah, the little musician, composed a new song about "Our house on the river Tauber." Rebecca, the poet of the family, wrote a six-line poem. Sarah began to plant rosebushes in the garden. And R. Meir studied the many applications of the young boys and men who wished to come and study with him.

The Call to Rothenburg

By the third day after their arrival, everyone felt so at home in the new surroundings, they might have lived there always. Meir thought it would be pleasant to have a family picnic. Sarah prepared the lunch, and they rented a boat and went out on the river Tauber for the day.

R. Meir enjoyed being on the water; it was calm and soothing. It pushed away the many problems and details that settling in a new house and a new town had brought, and the complexities of the school he was founding. Here on the water he watched the blue sky overhead, listened to the lapping of the water against the sides of the boat, and enjoyed the excitement of his two daughters as the spray tingled their soft and happy faces.

Sarah, his wife, watched all three of them, contentment in her heart now that her family was together again. She loved seeing the real joy the little girls plainly felt in getting reacquainted with their father. To herself she uttered a fervent prayer that the family would never be separated again.

Rebecca is just like her father, Sarah thought, full of a great enjoyment of life, curious about the world, eager to discover new ideas, constantly training her mind even when she's not aware of it. Deborah was more like herself, she decided. She was quieter, getting just as much pleasure out of life but in a more subdued way, allowing life to come to her rather than rushing into life's experiences. Rebecca will perhaps laugh more in her life, her mother thought, and Deborah will always feel sorrow more keenly.

Just now the girls were clinging to their father, laughing up into his face. "A story, Father, please," Rebecca teased. "Tell us a story."

"A story, a story!" her younger sister echoed.

R. Meir reached over and pulled Deborah up onto his right knee, and Rebecca up on his left knee. "So you want a story," he said. He flicked his forefinger under Rebecca's nose, then under Deborah's, and said, "Would you like to know how you happen to have that indentation there under your noses?"

"Oh yes. Oh yes." The little girls spoke together.

R. Meir smiled, looked up at his wife, caught her eye, and they smiled together. Then he said to his daughters, "Listen carefully and I'll tell you how we come to have dimples under our noses.

"The soul of every person lives in Paradise before the person is born. And while the soul is in Paradise, an Angel shows it all the beautiful things, all the delights and all the joys of Paradise. Then, when it is time for the soul to descend to earth to join the body it is going to live in, the soul must be made to forget everything it has seen in Paradise, or it could never live happily on earth. It must retain only a dim, half-forgotten, but always-to-be-pursued fragment of a memory, as if this higher life had been a dream. This dim memory makes it strive towards beauty and perfection on earth. To make the soul forget what it has seen in Paradise before it enters its earthly body, the Angel flicks the child under the nose

. . . causing this indentation here above the mouth . . . and the soul forgets all it has seen in Paradise."

R. Meir stopped and looked from one girl to the other.

"Oh," breathed Deborah. "That was a beautiful story."

"Tell us another," insisted Rebecca, leaning back blissfully against her father's arm.

"Well, one time," R. Meir said, "there was a man who was traveling in the desert. He was hungry. He was weary. And he was thirsty. Soon he came to a tree whose fruits were sweet and whose shade was pleasant; and beneath it flowed a little stream of water. He ate of the fruits, drank of the waters, and sat in the shade of the tree. He was refreshed and rested. When he was ready to continue on his journey, he said to the tree,

" 'O Tree, O Tree, how can I bless thee for the help you have given me? If I say to thee, may thy fruit be sweet, behold, thy fruits are already sweet. If I say to thee, may thy shade be beautiful, behold, thy shade is already beautiful. If I say to thee, thy sparkling stream shall flow smoothly, behold, thy sparkling stream already flows smoothly. How then may I bless thee?

" 'Ah,' the man said, 'let me bless thee in this way:- let every sapling that they plant from thee be just like thee.' "

R. Meir turned to look at the little girls. Deborah had fallen asleep. Rebecca turned dreamy eyes to her father and said,

"I like that story. It's just like a poem."

Sarah lifted Deborah gently from her father's arm so as not to awaken her. And then it was Rebecca's turn to tell her father a story.

The day passed too quickly, but happily. That day on the water restored to the little family the complete sense of oneness as a family, healing the wound of the separation of the past five years. The lonely parting was over. The family was together. The family would remain together now for all time.

By the end of the day they were sunburned, but happy. They settled down to the business of living in their new home. The little girls found that the first thing that was going to be very different from their life in Worms was that they would now receive regular lessons.

"But, Father," Rebecca said mischievously, "when we lived in Worms, mother gave us our lessons every day, but not so long and not so strict because everybody says little girls don't have to study as much as little boys."

R. Meir smiled at his daughter. She was just pretending. She loved to study. Ever since she had been big enough to hold a quill in her hand, she had been eager to learn to write. She seemed to have inherited from her father the art of composing poetry, and from babyhood on she had recited her little poems. But she had spent most of her time learning to write.

She had been taught to distinguish between different kinds of quills, how to sharpen them with her penknife, and told to keep her linen penwiper near her always. She had learned that the ink she used came from the gall of the oak tree, a little black ball made by an insect. This gall was soaked and boiled in water and produced a black ink that lasted a long time. She learned to use the tools of her craft very quickly and very well, and had spent a great deal of time learning and practicing her writing. Now, at the age of nine, she was considered to have a fine handwriting, particularly for a girl.

In the Middle Ages it was not considered important to educate little girls. But it could hardly be possible for a child of R. Meir—who was so great a scholar and came from a family of scholars—and a child of Sarah—who was well-educated for a woman and who also came from a family of scholars—it was hardly possible for a child of those parents not to receive a good education.

So R. Meir smiled now at his little daughter, saying, "Of course your mother gave you your lessons. And that is something for you to remember. For some day you will grow up and be married and have children of your own, and then you will know that you will have to teach your children their first lessons."

"Of course," little Deborah said quietly, her brown eyes big and serious as she gazed at her father. "The first music I ever learned I heard from my mama."

Meir laughed as he gathered both his daughters into his arms. "Some people think girls need no education," he said. "But I remember that in Bagdad in the twelfth century, about a hundred years ago, there was a man whose name was Samuel ben Ali. He was called a 'Prince of the Captivity.' This Samuel ben Ali of Bagdad had no sons . . ."

"Like you," Rebecca interrupted.

R. Meir nodded. "Like me. He had no sons. But—he had only *one* daughter, and I have *two*," he said triumphantly.

The two little girls looked at each other and smiled.

"Yes, indeed," their father said. "I have two daughters and he had only one. But, listen, girls." He paused and they both stood up straight, their eyes glued to his face, setting their lips firmly as if that would make them hear better. "Samuel ben Ali of Bagdad had only one daughter, but . . . she was a very well-educated woman. She was considered an expert in the study of the Bible and also in the Talmud."

"But what good did it do her to know the Bible and the Talmud?" Rebecca asked.

"She was able to teach other people," R. Meir said. "And this is remarkable—she was even permitted to teach boys and young men. As a rule it was not considered proper for a woman to teach men so she had to sit inside her house, and the boys had to sit outside the house, underneath a window. And, through the window, she gave them their lessons!"

Deborah smiled and Rebecca clapped her hands.

"How funny!" Rebecca shouted.

R. Meir smiled. "And I'll tell you about another famous woman. She lived in our old home city of Worms. She was the daughter of Rabbi Abraham, who was a cantor. Her name was Urania, and she used to preach sermons, and even the men listened to her."

Rebecca and Deborah smiled at each other. What this

woman, Urania of Worms, had done, didn't seem so remarkable to them. But their father was smiling—and it
was so wonderful to be here with their father—that they
smiled too.

"And then there was another woman, also from
Worms," their father continued. "Her name was Dulcie.
Her husband's name was Eliezer. And this Dulcie . . ."

"Isn't that a lovely name!" Deborah sighed.

"Sh!" Rebecca cautioned. "You mustn't interrupt
father."

"Dulcie is a lovely name," R. Meir said, "and she was
a lovely woman too, and very smart. She used to give
lectures to people on the Sabbath. And there have been
many women who were doctors. So you see, it *is* important for girls to get an education."

The little girls gazed quietly at their father for a moment, then Deborah said,

"I'll study hard and be a good musician."

And Rebecca shouted, "And I'll study my writing
over and over and over . . ."

The girls ran off, hand in hand, ready to start their
studying, except that, first, there was a wounded bird in
the garden that demanded their attention. They left their
father to get on with his work.

R. Meir's work was of importance to his people. In
the Middle Ages the Jews were entirely self-governed. In
whatever country they settled, the rulers agreed that the
Jews must govern themselves. It was true, of course, that
they had to obey the laws of the particular country in
which they lived, but only if their laws did not interfere

with the religious laws laid down in the Bible and the Talmud.

In whatever country they settled, they lived as a group apart. They were willing to pay for the privilege of settling in those countries, for protection of their lives and their properties, and for the right to engage in business. But they were not willing to give up their personal freedom, their principles of justice, or their code of law.

In most countries, therefore, they were given documents by the ruling prince or king which were called "Privilege-documents." These papers gave them the right to have their own government. They paid a price for these privilege-documents, but they were not unwilling to pay. Often, however, they were forced to pay more than they should have, since every prince and every king and every bishop felt that *he* had a right to tax the Jews.

In order to undertake this self-government and to pay for it, each community had to organize itself. The community established courts of justice; it claimed the right to make rules and to impose fines; to inflict punishment; to confiscate property. The Jewish community in Germany controlled the life of every Jew. It controlled his education, his religion and his economic, social and political life.

In Germany, especially, where the community enjoyed the freedom of self-government, they based their laws and their community life completely and exclusively on the Talmud. Since the talmudic laws had been written centuries earlier, they always needed interpretation so that they could be applied to the present life of the people. These interpretations created frequent disagreements among the scholars and so it was often necessary to appeal to higher authorities.

R. Meir of Rothenburg was one such authority.

He quickly became the chief judge of the Jews of the community of Rothenburg, and very soon many other communities came to rely upon his decisions, not only German communities but also those of Spain and Portugal, France, Hungary and England. From these countries he continually received letters asking for his opinion on matters of Jewish law. Hundreds and hundreds of such questions were directed to him every year. His answers (the answers of these authorities are known as "Responsa") are still studied today.

R. Meir came to Rothenburg at a critical time in the life of the Jews. Life had never been easy for them because the world around them was a completely Christian world, and often a fanatical Christian world. It was a time when the heads of the churches knew no sympathy for or had any understanding of any religious belief that was not based in Christianity. Judaism and Mohammedanism were considered to be as pagan as idolatry. The medieval Christians never ceased in their efforts to make the entire world Christian. So the Jews, who deeply loved their own faith, were under constant pressure by the powerful majority to throw away, to despise, and to declare false that which they loved.

Added to this religious pressure was an economic pressure. Every person who possessed authority in the Christian world considered the Jew his own special prey.

Every bishop, every prince and every king wanted to enrich himself at the expense of the Jews. So at times, besides the regular taxes which every citizen had to pay, the Jews were taxed three times more. This constant squeezing of his purse made it almost impossible for the Jew to live.

At the time when R. Meir came to Rothenburg, the Church and the State began a policy to crush the Jew completely. However, the Jews were not willing to accept this oppression without a struggle. They fought. They had to struggle against popes and bishops and kings and emperors; but they fought.

The person who remained in the thick of the fight was Rabbi Meir.

And the man who became his chief enemy was Rudolph—Rudolph the Emperor of Germany.

5

The Emperor and the Scholar

RUDOLPH I, the Emperor
of Germany, was born on May 1, 1218, at Limburg, into
the wealthy and powerful ruling house of the Hapsburgs.
His father was Albert IV, the count of Hapsburg. His
mother was Hedwig, the daughter of Ulrich, the count of
Kyburg.

When Rudolph was twenty-one his father died, leaving him in possession of vast estates. He added to his
wealth by marrying Gertrude, the daughter of Burkhard
III, the count of Hohenberg. Still more property came to
him from the Emperor Frederick II, who was his god-
father.

Rudolph seemed to have a Midas touch. Whatever he
touched turned to gold, and more and more wealth
flowed into his coffers, more and more property came

under his control, more and more titles and positions of power were his for the seizing. So that by the time he was fifty-five years old, he was the most powerful prince in southwestern Germany.

When the time came to elect a new Emperor, Rudolph was a strong contender for the position. His opponent was Ottakar II, King of Bohemia. But Rudolph was stronger than the Bohemian king. In addition to his own powerful position, he had the support of other influential princes: his brother-in-law, Frederick III of Hohenzollern, the burgrave of Nuremberg, Albert, the duke of Saxe-Lauenberg, and Louis II, the count palatine of the Rhine and duke of upper Bavaria.

Rudolph was elected Emperor and was crowned at Aix-la-Chapelle on October 24, 1273.

Once he became Emperor, Rudolph had to consolidate his position and gain strength quickly if he wanted to secure the succession of the house of Hapsburg. To do that he needed vast sums of money, and he turned to the one man who never failed him—a Jew, Amshel Oppenheimer.

Amshel Oppenheimer was able to help the Emperor financially because he had holdings in Amsterdam, in Vienna, in the Provence, the south of France. And so he was *able* to help Rudolph whenever he wanted money, but even more importantly, he was *willing* to send a steady stream of gold into the Emperor's bottomless reservoir because it helped the Jews if the Emperor was contented.

For one whole year Amshel Oppenheimer kept himself at the service of the Emperor. Then, one day, two things happened which sent him in haste to R. Meir of Rothenburg.

R. Meir by now, besides being considered the leader of the Jews of Germany, was also a very rich man. His family was wealthy and he had access to those monies; and besides, he was fortunate in that he knew how to make sound investments. He became a wealthy man in his own right. This was important to him; scholar that he was, he was nevertheless a practical man as well. He wanted his wife and daughters to have comfortable lives. He wanted also to be able to help people less fortunate than himself who constantly came to him for assistance.

It was a mild summer day, on the 7th of July in the year 1274, when Amshel Oppenheimer came traveling post-haste to R. Meir in Rothenburg. R. Meir and his wife were sitting in the garden going over certain school arrangements, when a servant came to announce Amshel Oppenheimer.

R. Meir and Sarah hurried to greet their guest. They brought him out into the garden, settled him comfortably, and asked for his family and for mutual friends. The servant was sent for Rebecca and Deborah so that they might greet their "uncle" Amshel. After a few pleasant moments, the girls returned to their study and the tea tray was set up in the garden.

Sarah poured Amshel a cup of tea, and laughingly added the third spoonful of sugar when he protested that two were not sufficient for his sweet tooth. She served her husband his tea. She passed around a plate of tiny cupcakes, and then she said,

"I know you two must have much to talk about, and I shall leave you . . ."

Smiling, she went into the house, leaving the two men sipping their tea in silence. They were glad for the few moments of relaxation, for they knew that when the conversation began in earnest the harsh light of reality would banish peace and quiet to the shadows. They sipped their tea, relished the little cakes, and listened to the silence. Finally, with a sigh, R. Meir set down his teacup and turned to Amshel Oppenheimer.

"A pleasant interlude," he said quietly, with a small smile. "But I know you did not travel all the way to Rothenburg to sip a cup of tea."

Amshel Oppenheimer sighed too, put down his teacup, and said, "Such tranquility is not the pattern of life in this thirteenth century. I bring you two important items of news, one good, one slightly troublesome."

He smiled a little twisted smile which made R. Meir laugh.

"Well, then," he said, "tell me the good news first."

Amshel Oppenheimer leaned forward and said slowly, "Today is the 7th day of July, the year 1274. Turn those numbers around. What happened on the 5th day of July in the year 1247?"

R. Meir smiled. "Ah, Amshel, you have always loved to play with numbers. What happened on the 5th day of July in 1247?" The smile left his face briefly as he concentrated. Then the smile returned in full force. "1247?

Why, the Pope made a declaration—yes, in 1247 Pope Innocent IV made his firm declaration to all the rulers of Christian lands—"

". . . Now, since we do not want the said Jews to be unjustly harassed . . ."

Amshel Oppenheimer intoned in a deep voice, and R. Meir continued,

". . . therefore we command that you show yourself favorably disposed and kindly towards them . . ."

and Amshel Oppenheimer continued,

". . . you shall not permit the Jews to be molested undeservedly!"

Amshel jumped to his feet and paced rapidly up and down in front of R. Meir.

"It hasn't been made public yet," he said in a voice made shrill by excitement. "But now, today, the new pope—Pope Gregory X, renewed that declaration!"

"Amshel!" R. Meir jumped to his feet. He grabbed his friend's arm. "Is that true?"

Amshel Oppenheimer nodded vigorously. "Yes. Yes. Pope Gregory has even amplified it. Listen to the terms of his declaration. He says that Jews are not to be made by brute force to undergo baptism, and that no injury is to be inflicted on their persons or their property."

"Too good to be true!" R. Meir too, in excitement, began to march up and down the garden, but only for a minute or two, and then he stopped and shook his head. His voice turned mournful and uncertain as he said,

"But Amshel, that declaration, that edict comes from the Pope, it is true, but will the Emperor heed it? Will Rudolph obey the Pope?"

"He will," Amshel said confidently. "After all, Rudolph owes the Jews a great deal. I have given him untold fortunes . . ."

R. Meir smiled slightly, rousing Amshel to protest: "But I have! I've given Rudolph vast sums—"

"I know." R. Meir put his hand gently on Amshel's arm. "I know, Amshel, and your fellow Jews know how much you have helped them by being so generous to the Emperor. But do you really think that Rudolph will now agree to the edict of Pope Gregory? If he really listens to those words—not to inflict injury on their property—why, he would lose his power of taxing them as heavily as he always has . . ."

Amshel Oppenheimer did not look directly at R. Meir, but down at the ground, and said quietly, "Now I must tell you the unpleasant piece of news . . ." He hesitated, sighed, and spoke. "Rudolph has asked for a loan" (his lips twisted on the word 'loan') "of three hundred thousand gold pieces . . ."

"Three hundred thousand!" R. Meir exclaimed. "But that is impossible . . ."

"Yes, impossible." Amshel Oppenheimer raised his eyes to his friend's face. "Impossible for one man to handle alone. And that is why I have come to you, Meir, for help—from you and your family."

R. Meir stood silent, thinking quickly, and then he

said slowly, "How much do you want from me and my family?"

"One hundred thousand."

R. Meir nodded briefly. "On one condition. That Rudolph will confirm this new decree of Pope Gregory."

Amshel Oppenheimer drew in his breath sharply in astonishment. "Meir! How dare we bargain with the Emperor?"

"How dare we not?" R. Meir said sharply. "You know how badly Rudolph has behaved to the Jews. One day he makes a tiny concession, and the next day he undermines it by a new and harsher decree. I am willing to go to my family and raise this money, Amshel, but on my condition—that Rudolph will ratify this decree of Pope Gregory."

R. Meir's decision stood firm, regardless of any argument Amshel Oppenheimer could bring forth.

"The Emperor must confirm Pope Gregory's decree!"

6

"Honor Thy Father"

It was agreed, then. Amshel Oppenheimer would promise to give the Emperor three hundred thousand pieces of gold on condition that he would ratify the edict of Pope Gregory, and that R. Meir would try to raise one hundred thousand gold pieces from his rich family.

He quickly formulated a plan. He would not make his plea by letter, but in person. He would travel over Germany to see his rich uncles, but, he would not travel alone. He would take his daughter Rebecca.

Rebecca had become his constant companion and, surprisingly, his secretary. From the time they had first come to Rothenburg to live, she was so happy to be reunited with her father that she had determined that nothing again would ever part them. She would make herself necessary to him. She would make herself indispensable. Then they would never again be separated.

But how could she do this? She would develop her handwriting, she decided. She would help her father with his letters. She knew that a great deal of mail came to their house every day. Night after night, R. Meir spent long hours at his desk, answering those letters. Even in the hot summer evenings, when the family rested out of doors in Sarah's beautiful rose-garden, he would stay indoors, writing and writing, deaf to their pleas to come out and enjoy the balmy summer evening and the scent of the white roses.

So Rebecca determined that she would become her father's scribe. She would develop so beautiful a handwriting that her father would never desire any other. She devoted herself intently to her studies. Hour after hour, day after day, when other girls were playing with their dolls or learning fine sewing, Rebecca practiced her handwriting. She practiced so diligently that before long her writing of the Hebrew script was clear and beautiful, and above all, readable.

On the day of her eleventh birthday she had received the greatest birthday present she would ever receive. In honor of her birthday she was wearing a new white dress. But just because it was her birthday did not mean that she would excuse herself from her daily writing practice. She began to sharpen her quill. So intent was she upon keeping the sharp penknife from snipping her fingers that she didn't hear her father approaching her desk.

When he saw she was sharpening quills, he waited before speaking to her. If startled, she might cut herself. When she had the last quill prepared, and had put the knife carefully away, he spoke.

"Is our birthday girl going to work today?"

At his first word she jumped to her feet and threw her arms around him. "Father! Father! I didn't hear you come!"

"You were absorbed."

R. Meir chuckled as the willowy girl stopped trying to crush his ribs, stepped back, and laughed into his eyes.

"Father, look how tall I've grown!"

He pulled her head against his shoulder.

"Right up to my shoulder. Too bad. Too bad." He shook his head sadly.

"Too bad?" Rebecca stared at her father. "Too bad? Oh no, Father. What's bad about my growing tall?"

He smiled. "Nothing. Except that it means that soon I won't have a little girl-daughter. I'll have a young-lady daughter."

She giggled.

"Young ladies don't giggle."

She giggled again. "But I'm not a young lady yet. I'm only eleven years old. So I can still giggle."

They laughed together, he deep-throated, she with the high, unformed voice of a young girl.

" 'There is a time for tears and a time for joy,' " R. Meir quoted from King Solomon. " 'There is a time to play and a time to work.' "

Rebecca's face lost its carefree expression. The look

she turned on her father's handsome face was serious, adult.

"Some people may say," said R. Meir, "that age eleven is too young for a girl to begin to work."

"Oh no." But Rebecca objected so quietly that the two small words might not have reached her father's ears.

"And perhaps it is," he continued. "But you have been so serious about your studies, particularly about your study of writing, that I venture to say that what I am going to propose to you will not dismay you, young as you are."

Rebecca kept her brown eyes fastened to her father's, scarcely daring to breathe.

"As you know," R. Meir said, "my correspondence has become heavier and heavier with each passing year. I cannot continue unless I have help."

Rebecca made a quick movement with her right hand. Her father smiled.

"And I wondered, Rebecca, if perhaps you could help me."

"Oh, I can! I can!"

R. Meir held up his hand. "Not too fast. You must know what you're agreeing to. It means you will have less time for play . . ."

"Oh, let me help! I don't care about play! Let me help! Please, Father!"

"It will be difficult work," he warned her. "Every day my correspondence increases. Letters from Toledo, Spain, letters from London, England, letters from Paris."

Letters from all over Europe flowed into Rothenburg into the study of R. Meir ben Baruch. He studied each letter with care and gave special attention to each request, reading the ancient source-materials and the new opinions, sifting, weighing, deciding.

Rebecca said to him, "Father, why do you have to keep studying the Talmud so hard? I'm sure that by now you must know everything in it."

R. Meir laughed. "No man will ever know *everything* that is contained in the Talmud. Besides," and now he became completely serious. "I must never rely on my memory. These questions which come to me for decision must be answered carefully. Look at these letters, Rebecca."

He held up four for her to see.

"Here is a letter from the Jews of Moravia. This is their problem:- The King of Bohemia, Wenceslaus, has appointed his son Ottokar as margrave of Moravia. That means he gave over to his son the income from the taxes imposed on the Jews of that territory. And because of that, a serious dispute has arisen between the Jewish communities of Bohemia and Moravia over the payment of taxes. In former times, the Jews of Bohemia and Moravia paid their taxes to the king together, each community contributing its share. Now I must decide whether it is right for the community of Moravia to be permitted to stop paying taxes to the king, since it must now pay taxes to Prince Ottokar."

He put down the letters and continued. "Questions come to me on every kind of problem, on real estate

matters, inheritance difficulties, partnership entangle-
ments, marriage contracts—on every subject imagin-
able. And I must know the answers, Rebecca. I must
know the correct answers."

She nodded gravely. Then she smiled. "Oh you do.
You always know the correct answers."

R. Meir smiled at her confidence in him. "If you become my scribe, you will have to work very, very hard."

She nodded solemnly. "I want to work with you,
Father. I want that more than anything else in the
world."

So, to the amazement of his family, his friends, and
his pupils, his eleven-year-old daughter became his
scribe. Her dream had come true. Now she would never
be separated from her father. Now they would work
together side by side, forever.

And so they had done for four busy, happy years.
Wherever R. Meir had traveled during these years, Rebecca had accompanied him. Therefore, now, when he
set out to go to his uncles to raise money for the Emperor, Rebecca went with him.

They went first to R. Samuel b. Baruch in Bamberg,
then to R. Menahem b. Natronai in Würzburg. These
visits were delightful ones for the family. They were
happy to see their nephew, R. Meir, and teased Rebecca
about her important position as her father's scribe. From
Meir's point of view, the visits were highly successful
because each uncle pledged the money he had come
for.

These pledges came to his hand also from his other

uncles whom they traveled to see, R. Judah b. Moses Ha-Kohen in Mayence, and the two uncles who lived in Cologne, R. Yakar b. Samuel Ha-Levi and R. Baruch b. Urshraga. The pledges were offered, and a warm welcome in each home. But their warmest welcome and their most joyous visit took place in Worms at the home of R. Meir's father, R. Baruch.

But there in his father's home, R. Meir was sad, though he concealed his sadness. It was his father who made him sad. Suddenly R. Baruch seemed to his son to be very old, very, very old, and failing in health. His brilliant mind was as keen as ever, but R. Meir saw the hand of death fluttering about his father's frail body.

They returned home from their journeys, R. Meir feeling both gratified and grieved—gratified because all the money that he needed for the rapacious Rudolph was pledged to him—and grieved because he knew his father's life was drawing to its end.

He had been home from his travels one month when, on the same day, two messages came to him. One message was from Amshel Oppenheimer.

"The Emperor Rudolph is not easy to convince about ratifying the decree set down by Pope Gregory. He demands that you seek an audience with him. He will be in Vienna in three days time and demands your presence there."

The second message brought the sad news of the death of R. Meir's father.

He left at once for Worms.

7

The Generosity of the Emperor

"**T**HE EMPEROR will have to be satisfied," Sarah said softly to Amshel Oppenheimer.

"But Meir cannot do this to the Emperor!" Amshel exclaimed.

When he had received R. Meir's message saying that he would not be in Vienna to attend Rudolph the Emperor, Amshel had hurried to Rothenburg. There he found only Sarah, with her soft answers. Now, in his agitation, he kept striding about the room, not accepting Sarah's offer to sit down or to have tea—just striding back and forth, back and forth.

"My dear Sarah, I must insist—he cannot do this to the Emperor!"

Sarah smiled wistfully. "But my dear Amshel Oppenheimer, he has done it. Now please, dear friend, calm yourself. You know very well that Meir could and would do nothing else but what he has done. His father has died. Meir has gone to Worms for the funeral. He will remain there for the full mourning period. And nothing you will say, nor the Emperor, nor the Pope, will bring him back from Worms one hour sooner than he deems proper."

Amshel Oppenheimer turned sorrowful eyes to her. "Then tell him when he returns, please, that the audience has been cancelled, that Rudolph the Emperor will *not* ratify the edict of Pope Gregory."

When the full mourning period for his father had ended, R. Meir returned to his home, and Sarah told him of Amshel's visit and his message. R. Meir listened quietly, shrugged slightly, and said softly,

"It hath been told thee in Sacred Scripture, 'Honor thy father and thy mother.'"

Many men lead useful, talented lives. They are great lawyers, or fine doctors, or accomplished musicians. But Meir of Rothenburg had many varied abilities. He was a capable, brilliant lawyer in talmudic law, an unofficial supreme justice for the Jews of Europe. That alone could have kept him busy. That alone did keep him busy. And it might have been sufficient to give any other man the feeling and the knowledge that his life was being spent in the most useful way possible.

But it was not sufficient for Meir, not for a man with so creative a mind. Learning, studying, the development of the mind—that he felt was every man's obligation to himself. But the passing on of that learning was a man's obligation to his fellow-man. Meir was a teacher by nature. He had been able to amass a great deal of knowledge in his lifetime. And he felt it was his duty to pass on this knowledge to others.

To fulfill this purpose he had opened his school in Rothenburg. Young boys of about fourteen years, and young men from fifteen years and up came to him from all over Germany and France to study. Since these boys did not live in Rothenburg, but came from afar, he had to make it possible for them to live in his home.

He established his college in the large twenty-one-room house in Rothenburg. Before the first year was over, all of the twenty-one rooms were filled. Still more and more students came, and they had to be lodged with friends and neighbors.

As Meir ben Baruch himself had once been eager to go to France to study with famous teachers, now boys and young men from all over Europe were eager to come to Rothenburg to study with him. Rabbi Meir was happy in this work. He loved young people, and he loved to see their minds grow. He loved to impart his knowledge to them.

Of course, it happened, as it always does, that certain young men became his special pupils. The first of these was Mordecai b. Hillel. He came to Rabbi Meir's school when the college had been in existence for six years. He was already married and had children, but he desired to continue his studies.

The Captive Rabbi

Mordecai* had been a friend of Meir's brother, Abraham.** The two men, both brilliant scholars, had studied together for years, pooling some of their best ideas, stimulating each other's mind, encouraging each other in their chosen work.

One evening, as they sat up late over a glass of wine and a piece of sponge cake, after having studied for the long hours of a summer's evening, Abraham said suddenly,

"Mordecai, you are wasting time here."

Mordecai, in surprise, looked up at his friend. He felt a tight band of fatigue around his head from their concentrated study. His eyes burned from hours of poring over the small, irregular writing on parchment. Then how could his friend Abraham accuse him of wasting his time?

An angry retort rose to his lips, but he looked at his friend's red-rimmed eyes and saw that he, too, was weary with fatigue. So instead of an angry rebuke, he answered with a smile.

"There is a deeper meaning in your words, friend Abraham, than my tired mind understands. We are both weary from this night's study. Be good enough to speak out plainly."

Abraham smiled too, as he lifted his wine-glass to his lips. He sipped the sweet liquid, letting it roll on his tongue so that he might enjoy it longer.

"I repeat, Mordecai," he said. "You are wasting your

---

* He later became famous for his great code called *The Mordecai*.
** Abraham's book was called *Sefer Sinai*.

time. You should go to Rothenburg and study with my brother Meir."

Surprise kept Mordecai silent for a moment. He knew there was a strong family bond between Abraham and Meir. Still, it wasn't necessary for Abraham to demean himself by making Meir out to be so much greater.

"Meir is a great scholar, Mordecai," Abraham said softly, "a great, great scholar. In my family, it is true, we do not lack for great scholars. But Meir is the greatest of them all."

It is true, Mordecai reflected, nibbling on a piece of the cake. He had always heard men of learning praise Meir, praise him above his brother Abraham, above his famous uncles, even above his illustrious father.

"In the special work you are doing, Mordecai," Abraham's pleasant voice continued, "you could get a great deal of help from my brother. He receives questions from every land—from England and France and even from Spain. His responsa are becoming world famous. And it may be that in the law codes on which you are working, he could be of help to you."

So it was that Mordecai b. Hillel went to Rothenburg with his wife and his five children, and his wife's young brother, Meir Ha-Kohen.

On the day they arrived, another visitor came, unannounced—Amshel Oppenheimer.

"Meir." Amshel Oppenheimer spoke quickly, evidently under great stress. "Meir, the Emperor is here. He is here, here in Rothenburg. He claims to have come on some very important business. But Meir, I know!—I know he came expressly to see you."

"Amshel, Amshel. Control yourself. Calm yourself. You are too excited—"

"No, Meir, don't stop me. Listen, my friend. I believe, I earnestly, honestly believe that Rudolph has come here especially to see you, though of course he would deny that stoutly. I believe he is ready and willing to ratify Pope Gregory's decree."

R. Meir's eyes lighted up. "Amshel, that would be so good, so good—"

"Will you come with me—now?"

"Certainly!"

They went without delay, in a handsome carriage drawn by four white horses, to the palace of the Governor where Rudolph the Emperor was a guest.

The audience that day was an historical one, a memorable one. As R. Meir and Amshel Oppenheimer rode into the courtyard, they looked up to the balcony and saw the Emperor standing there rigidly, watching their approach.

He stood outlined against the sky, a tall man with a pale face and a prominent nose.

Then, he turned and entered the palace through the long balcony window.

By the time R. Meir and Amshel Oppenheimer had entered the palace and had been ushered into his presence, Rudolph was already seated in a high-backed chair. It was upholstered in green velvet, and against it his pale face looked paler than usual and his large nose dominated his waxy-looking face. But his eyes were keen and alert, and took in every detail of the two men standing before him.

"Amshel Oppenheimer I have known for many years," Rudolph said, and his voice was pleasant, quiet. "And you, sir, must be Rabbi Meir of Rothenburg."

R. Meir inclined his head slightly.

"I have long heard of the wisdom and the greatness of the Rabbi," Rudolph said courteously.

R. Meir inclined his head again in a small bow and answered, "And I have heard of the piety and the generosity of the Emperor." He smiled.

The Emperor returned the smile. "Now we may test the wisdom of the Rabbi."

R. Meir's smile deepened. "As we may now test the generosity of the Emperor."

The Emperor, smiling, led the conversation into one field after another, probing the Rabbi's knowledge of German law, of the new school of philosophy which was becoming so popular in Spain, of the field of astronomy. He would ask, it seemed, of every matter except that which interested his two visitors. Amshel Oppenheimer was impatient, and a little angry, feeling that the Emperor was toying with them as a cat toys with a mouse. But R. Meir's spirits rose with every passing moment. He realized that the Emperor was in a friendly mood, inclined to listen sympathetically to the arguments he would present for the confirming of the Pope's edict, and that Rudolph was also genuinely interested in this conversation, which was intellectual rather than practical.

A servant entered, bringing a bowl of fruit. Another servant followed, carrying a wine bottle and glasses. The social amenities were being observed, and every action of Rudolph's indicated his pleasure in their company.

Finally, the conversation, led skillfully by R. Meir into the economic conditions in Germany, turned to the matter directly at hand. Suddenly the Emperor leaned forward, smiled warmly, and said,

"Rabbi Meir, we shall confirm the edict of Pope Gregory."

8

The Duren Case

"IT WAS Rabbi Meir's doing," Amshel Oppenheimer said. "It was Rabbi Meir's doing, I tell you, all his!"

R. Meir and Amshel Oppenheimer had returned from the audience with the Emperor. They were in the parlor now, surrounded by the family: Sarah and Rebecca and Deborah and Mordecai b. Hillel and his wife and his wife's young brother, Meir Ha-Kohen.

"The Emperor said as much," Amshel Oppenheimer said, still in his excited way. "He needed no urging, believe me . . . but of his own free will he said he would ratify the edict of Pope Gregory."

"I am not so easy in my mind," R. Meir said, frowning. "I fear Rudolph may have been tricking us."

"But he did ratify Gregory's edict," Amshel insisted.

R. Meir nodded reluctantly. "Yes, and he has even gone one step further, my friends. I just wish we could trust him. But, Rudolph is willing to ratify the Pope's edict, and especially does he confirm and declare that if a Jew is arrested for any crime, he may be condemned only on the *valid* evidence of Jews and Christians . . ."

"And you know," Amshel interrupted in his enthusiasm, "you know that's never happened before."

It was a day for rejoicing. But finally, since life must always resume its usual tenor, Amshel Oppenheimer departed for his home, and R. Meir and his household settled down to their daily chores and work.

Unknown to R. Meir, another warfare was being waged in his own household. The two protagonists were Rebecca and Mordecai b. Hillel's brother-in-law, Meir Ha-Kohen. Meir Ha-Kohen was then about fifteen years old, as was Rebecca.

Rebecca had grown into a beautiful young lady. She was tall and slender, and her glossy black hair and brown sparkling eyes gave vitality to her strong, oval face, with its high cheekbones and beautifully shaped mouth. No one, however—not even her father, nor her mother, nor her sister—no one ever saw how finely shaped Rebecca's mouth was, because she was always laughing, or at worst, always smiling.

Until Meir Ha-Kohen came. Then Rebecca learned to frown. Because almost immediately, they became rivals; they became rivals for her father's attention.

R. Meir and Mordecai b. Hillel, however, became friends, as fast as Rebecca and the young Meir became enemies. It did not take R. Meir long to find the same fine qualities in Mordecai that his brother Abraham had found. He respected Mordecai's quality of mind so quickly and deeply that almost immediately, they studied as equals. In fact, they almost never had a relationship of teacher and disciple. Mordecai was grateful to Abraham for having urged him to study with R. Meir.

This was not the case with Meir Ha-Kohen, of course. He had come with his brother-in-law to be one of R. Meir's pupils. But young Meir was, after all, only fifteen years old. Further, he would never possess the depths of wisdom of his brother-in-law. But what he lacked in brilliance he made up for in loyalty. Meir Ha-Kohen adored R. Meir from the first day he saw him, adored him and desired only one thing—to serve him, completely and absolutely.

The rivalry between Rebecca and himself was caused by the fact that Meir Ha-Kohen also had a beautiful handwriting. For four busy years, Rebecca had been her father's constant companion and secretary. Then came Meir Ha-Kohen—Meir Ha-Kohen with *his* beautiful handwriting.

R. Meir was delighted to find this young man of fifteen who could be of so much help to him. Before very long he was dictating as much correspondence to Meir Ha-Kohen as he was to Rebecca. Meir Ha-Kohen quickly became as jealous of Rebecca as she was of him. He couldn't understand why the Master should dictate his responsa to a mere girl. He, Meir Ha-Kohen, wrote a better hand and he was a student. And further, what did a mere girl know about talmudic law?

An intense rivalry developed between R. Meir's

daughter and his pupil. Everyone in the college, everyone in the stone house was aware of it—except R. Meir himself. He was so occupied with conducting his college, being the head of the community of the city of Rothenburg, and acting as chief judge of European Jewry, that he had no time to take notice of the undeclared warfare being waged right before his eyes.

He went to bed very late at night. Every light in every window of the walled city was darkened long before R. Meir was willing to put aside his work. There was so much to be done in the world. The hours of the day passed too quickly. The evening hours must be used, and some of the night hours.

And so R. Meir robbed sleep of some of its hours, and worked long into the night, until from sheer exhaustion his fingers grew lax, the quill dropped out of his hand, and the book was knocked from the table as his head fell heavily upon it. Then he would rouse himself long enough to take off his clothes, extinguish the oil-lamp, and fall into bed and into a quick, dreamless sleep.

Then, just as dawn broke, R. Meir awoke from his few hours of rest, to begin again. Each day brought new hours, new ideas, new creativity. A day and its work was reckoned precious to him.

It is no wonder, therefore, absorbed as he was in fitting three lifetimes into one, that he did not notice that his daughter's beautiful smile had been more and more replaced by a frown, and that Meir, his pupil-scribe, was becoming increasingly short-tempered.

This animosity between R. Meir's two scribes went on

for three years. Toward the end of the third year, Deborah, the younger sister, put an end to it. Deborah was known in the family and amongst their friends as the peace-maker. She was more delicate than Rebecca, quieter, shyer, but firm in all her convictions.

Just before Rebecca's eighteenth birthday, when she became engaged to marry Solomon b. Isaac, Deborah decided it was time for the silly quarrel to end.

Though it was mid-winter, she brought the two antagonists together in the center of the rose-garden, so that their conversation could not be overheard. Because it was cold and the air was clear and fine, they needed to talk only in the lowest of voices to be heard, standing, as they were, so close together.

"Now, then," Deborah said, "this whole situation is a piece of nonsense and must be stopped immediately."

"Indeed." Meir Ha-Kohen looked down at the sixteen-year-old girl. "Please, Deborah, go away and play with your dolls and stop disturbing your elders . . ."

"How dare you treat my sister like a baby!" Rebecca lashed out at him.

Meir Ha-Kohen turned furiously to her, ready to blast her with a heated charge.

But Deborah said quietly, softly, "I have something to say. I forbid either of you to utter one syllable until I have finished."

She stopped. Rebecca turned to her younger sister without speaking. Meir Ha-Kohen half turned his back on her. But he, too, remained silent.

Deborah spoke her piece. "You, Meir, should perhaps

be more ashamed of your sullen actions than Rebecca. You are a man. You are counted a man, at least. You study to be a scholar, and I have heard my father say that you are a good scholar. Well, then? If you are truly a scholar who is wise enough to study the Talmud, why are you not wise enough not to quarrel with a woman?"

She paused. But Meir Ha-Kohen only shrugged his shoulders, at least indicating that he had heard.

Deborah turned to Rebecca. "And you, Rebecca. I am surprised at you. You should have better manners. You are engaged to be married. How can you act so childishly? The idea of you two, acting like silly children instead of grownups, carrying on a quarrel which darkens the life of the whole family. And believe me, the only reason it darkens our lives is because we try so hard to keep Father from hearing about it."

Rebecca half turned from her sister so as to avoid her steady gaze.

"There is so much work to do for Father," Deborah said. "He works so hard. He has so many responsibilities. I should think that you would both be so thrilled to be taking a mite of the burden off his shoulders. And you are. I know it. I know you are both proud of the work you do. Then why not be friends? Being friends is so much nicer than being enemies."

Rebecca laughed softly. "You think so because you're the sweet, darling Deborah . . ."

Meir Ha-Kohen half turned back to growl, "Some people are made for enmity. They love the battle . . ."

"That's not so!" Rebecca cried. "Deborah is right! I'd

much rather be friends with you, Meir, really, truly, honestly I would. And I'd love to know how you get the downward stroke of the Kof so thick . . ."

Meir Ha-Kohen turned to face Rebecca. "Well, I'd rather be friends too, you know." Then, eagerly, "Rebecca, I'll gladly show you the thick downward stroke of the Kof but on one condition. Will you please tell me how you get that graceful curl on the top of the Lamed?"

"Oh yes!" Rebecca laughed. "It's easy . . ."

Deborah started to walk away from them. "You see, it is easy to be friends. Besides, there is enough work for both of you. There is too much work for one. You should each be glad of the work the other does. There is enough work for both."

"She's right," Meir Ha-Kohen said.

"Deborah's always right," Rebecca said, her laugh ringing out in the clear air.

Deborah turned her head to speak to them over her shoulder. "Shake hands and be friends."

They shook hands, out in the clear, cold air of the winter day in the rose-garden. And from that day on Rebecca and Meir Ha-Kohen were friends.

Soon something happened which cemented the new friendship. R. Meir began a new career, one of travel. Sometimes it was simpler for him when settling a law case to go to the community in need of aid, rather than attempt to decide the case by correspondence. Both of his scribes accompanied him on these travels, and both were happy.

Rebecca had an inner satisfaction. She had promised

herself never to be separated from her father, and now she could accompany him wherever he went. Besides, she had inherited his spirit of adventure, his love of travel, and his interest in new situations. Meir Ha-Kohen also was happy to journey with R. Meir. A deep bond had developed between these two men. Had R. Meir ever dreamed of having a son, he would have dreamed of a son like Meir Ha-Kohen, whose life was devoted to serving him. His service was guided by a complete dedication to his master, loyalty of mind, consecration of heart, and devotion of the spirit. Wherever R. Meir felt it was his duty to be, Meir Ha-Kohen wanted to be there too.

Therefore this new career of traveling suited all three. R. Meir was presently involved in a case that had started in Rothenburg, and then shuttled back and forth between Rothenburg and Duren.

Three weeks earlier, a short, thin, underfed, unhappy-looking young man, whose name was Jacob ben Moses, had appeared at R. Meir's house. If Rebecca had opened the door, she might have sent Jacob to one of her father's older students to handle his case, because her father was much, much too busy to take on another task.

As it was, however, Deborah opened the door. Deborah was soft-hearted and she could not bear the pleading in the stricken eyes of the half-starved bundle of misery seeking help. She brought him to her father.

Rebecca was at her writing-desk, busily engaged with the letters R. Meir had dictated to her the day before.

Meir Ha-Kohen was seated at his writing desk, making
notes about R. Meir's dictation on some legal matters.
And R. Meir was studying four scrolls which were un-
rolled on his desk.

A quick glance was enough to indicate the pressure of
work being undertaken in that room. The young man
hesitated on the threshold. But before he could step back
and escape, Deborah had captured her father's attention.

"Father dear, this young man needs your help."

R. Meir's eyes leaped from the manuscript he was
studying to the thin face of the young man in the doorway. Instantly he was on his feet, moving towards Jacob,
while Deborah gave the young man a gentle push into
the room.

Rebecca and Meir Ha-Kohen stopped writing, put
down their pens and flexed their stiffened fingers, glad
for a chance to rest their cramped arms and aching
backs. R. Meir handled this startled, frightened, wasted
individual with courtesy and gentleness. One look at the
fearful eyes, the pinched lips and the hunched shoulders
told the story of a man tossed carelessly by a remorseless
fate into a turbulent sea of life for which he had never
been prepared. And his story, when it came, haltingly
and nervously, testified to the onlooker's quick estimate
that this man was overwhelmed merely by the task of
living.

"My name is Jacob ben Moses," he said slowly, in a
low mumble, when R. Meir had seated him near his
desk. "My father—Rabbi Moses—"

R. Meir knew of Rabbi Moses, and knew that this

young man came from a poverty-stricken home. His story, when R. Meir succeeded in pulling it out of him, was typical, yet surprising.

Somehow, this poverty-stricken boy had become engaged to marry a wealthy girl, Leah, the daughter of R. Judah of Duren. One mystery was never cleared up: how it had happened that the wealthy R. Judah of Duren had betrothed his daughter to this unattractive, poor, wretched boy. That the betrothal had been made without R. Judah's ever having seen Jacob ben Moses was obvious. He certainly was not the husband for a beautiful, vivacious but spoiled darling like Leah of Duren. By nature he was morose, suspicious, and without humor. But he had been betrothed to Leah, and betrothal then was almost as binding as marriage.

At the time of the engagement, R. Judah of Duren had promised Jacob ben Moses not only to give him his daughter in marriage, but to support him; to clothe him and to feed him and to take care of him. A year and a half earlier, R. Judah had sent for Jacob to come to Duren to live.

Jacob had gone. Leah's family, after taking one look at Jacob, had been bitterly disappointed. Leah was indignant that her father should have given her so miserable a fiancé. R. Judah was mortified at having to acknowledge Jacob as a member of his family. Yet he had kept his promise to feed and clothe him—for one year.

It was not a happy year for Jacob. Leah would scarcely acknowledge his presence. R. Judah never found time for him. Leah's mother wept whenever she saw him. And Leah's cousins slyly mocked her for having such an ugly, unpleasant fiancé. For Jacob this year was one of humiliation.

To add to his mortification—and to his chagrin—at the end of the year, R. Judah sent him packing back to Rothenburg.

"Without your wife?" Rebecca asked, shocked.

Jacob nodded dumbly.

"But you must insist that she come here and live with you," Meir Ha-Kohen said gently.

"Oh, I have," Jacob cried. "But she will not come." And then, with his only show of defiance, "And I will not free her!"

R. Meir immediately wrote to R. Judah of Duren, demanding that Jacob's bride be sent to Rothenburg. R. Judah refused, and R. Meir decided that he himself must go to Duren to settle the case.

R. Meir, Rebecca, and Meir Ha-Kohen sent off on horseback for Duren. All travel on the roads was dangerous, and Meir Ha-Kohen always cantered on in advance to spy out the land. But they encountered no trouble until they reached Duren. The trouble they found there was in the stubbornness of R. Judah and his family.

R. Meir, who was greatly respected, was received with all courtesy. Judah's home was richly furnished, well cared for, and his hospitality was as fine as his home. But his mind was closed to logic or reason, or pity.

"But you promised," R. Meir insisted. "You promised your daughter to Jacob ben Moses."

"Let him divorce* my daughter," R. Judah said harshly.

"He wants Leah to come to Rothenburg and live as his wife," R. Meir said.

"Have you seen the miserable hovel in which he lives?" R. Judah asked. "How could I permit my daughter, who is used to every luxury, to live under such wretched conditions? I am being fair and just," he said pompously, "when I ask of Jacob that he come here to live."

R. Meir smiled. That smile nettled R. Judah.

"Why do you smile?"

"Isn't it true that you have sent your servants to Rothenburg, to warn Jacob that if he dares to return here, you will have him beaten within an inch of his life?"

"Indeed not," sputtered R. Judah. "How can you accuse me of such a thing? Indeed not!"

"No?" R. Meir smiled. "Then carry out your contract."

"No!"

R. Meir rose, not troubling to conceal his anger. "Just because you are rich and powerful, you think you can take base advantage of this helpless young man. And I say no! The talmudic law is the same for the rich as it is for the poor, and the same for the poor as it is for the rich. Your daughter must come to Rothenburg as Jacob's wife."

"No!"

---

* Since betrothal was considered as sacred as marriage, the only way an engagement could be broken was by actual divorce, and only a husband could divorce a wife (not the wife the husband).

This was hardly the end of the case. It dragged on for a number of years, with other rabbis becoming involved on the side of the rich family. Only R. Meir of Rothenburg fought for the poor young man, insisting upon justice. He would have continued to defend his charge, neglecting his own health and work and fighting a hopeless battle, except that young Jacob resolved the situation all by himself. He died of pneumonia.

The pneumonia was due to neglect which could have been avoided by help from R. Judah of Duren, help which he had promised and had failed to give.

R. Meir was bitter, so bitter that he was on the point of excommunicating R. Judah of Duren. But memory stopped him, the memory of a bonfire in Paris which burned the Talmuds, caused by the hatred of an excommunicated Jew. R. Meir stayed his hand. R. Judah of Duren remained an influential member of his community. His daughter, Leah, eventually married a man who was everything poor Jacob was not and could never have been.

Jacob went to his grave unmourned, and forgotten—by everyone but R. Meir.

9

The Horned Hat

"Our God and God of our fathers,
    Forgive, I beseech Thee,
    The trespass Thy people have wrought unto Thee,
    And let not Thine anger wax hot at Thy
        children's iniquity."*

R. MEIR was dictating a poem to Rebecca. It would be a prayer for the Day of Atonement, and his mind was filled with the solemn thought which he sought to express. Rebecca sat as quietly as she could, scarcely daring to breathe, not wanting to interrupt the flow of her father's words. The only sounds in the room were his voice and the scratching of her quill on the parchment.

* Poem written by R. Meir of Rothenburg, *Service of the Synagogue, Eve of Atonement,* Routledge & Sons, London, 1904.

A bird flew to the windowsill, perched, blinked its little eyes rapidly, gave out one sharp "tweet," and was on the wing and gone before R. Meir was even aware of it. Rebecca smiled. Her father's deep, melodious voice continued:-

> "Forgive, I beseech Thee,
>> Their pride; give them life from the fountain
>> with Thee.
>> Repent of the doom, and lift from Thine
>> hosts their iniquity."

R. Meir paused to search for the proper phrase, and the stillness was broken by the high-pitched voice of a little child.

"Mama! Mama! Where are you?"

Joel, Rebecca's four-year-old boy, came running into the room.

The year was 1267. A good many years had passed since Meir Ha-Kohen had become R. Meir's pupil and since he and Rebecca had fought their silent warfare over the privilege of being R. Meir's scribe. Deborah had been right—there *was* enough work to keep both of them occupied. There was more than enough now, since in addition to the correspondence which grew heavier year by year, R. Meir was engaged in his own literary work.

He was a Tosafist, a writer of "additional notes" to the Talmud. He not only studied the Talmud minutely, so as to know it perfectly, but he also wrote many additional notes to clarify difficult points, to make it easier for other scholars to study, and for all Jews to interpret all the law contained in it correctly. There were, after all, many complicated sections in the Talmud, and many difficulties too, ambiguities perhaps, lack of clarification. Whatever the difficulty, R. Meir studied it and then brilliantly explained it.

A scholar, however, could not presume that he was the only one who had found the difficulties or solved them. Before writing out his explanations, he would perhaps wish to consult with another Tosafist. Sometimes the matter was so difficult to clarify that it required an actual debate between two or more Tosafists, a learned debate and discussion before they were willing to agree on the proper explanation.

Another famous talmudic scholar, Solomon ben Adret, was a contemporary of R. Meir of Rothenburg. Solomon ben Adret lived in Spain and devoted the greater part of his study to these explanatory notes to the Talmud. These two famous scholars carried on a considerable correspondence. At times they debated a difficult point and at other times held a discussion, always respecting their colleague's scholarship and judgment. The writing of the Tosfos added a fourth side to the three-sided life R. Meir already led.

R. Meir was also a great poet. He delighted in composing poetry for religious services, and he loved to write rhymed verse about the Talmud, about life, and about the Bible. His was a mind that was never satisfied, but continued to search for new ideas, new justice, and new modes of thought. His accomplishments were numerous.

Although occupied with this literary life of extreme creativity, R. Meir continued to build up his college year after year.

Rebecca was married to Solomon b. Isaac, and Deborah was married to Moses b. Simon. Both girls had stayed on in the big stone house in Rothenburg. Neither wished to leave her parents, and each husband had kindly consented to settle in R. Meir's home. Thus Rebecca was able to continue to act as her father's scribe, even though she now had three children, two little boys and a girl.

Mordecai b. Hillel had left the college some time ago and had gone to Nuremberg with his wife and five children,* leaving his brother-in-law behind.

Meir Ha-Kohen would not leave R. Meir. His teacher was his whole life. When he was twenty-one, he married a sweet, shy girl named Helena, and requested permission of R. Meir to continue living in his house with Helena. R. Meir was happy to give that permission and to add Helena to his household. And because Rebecca and Deborah always felt as though Meir Ha-Kohen was their brother, they welcomed Helena as another sister.

Mordecai b. Hillel's place was quickly taken. When one of R. Meir's favorite pupils left, another exceptionally gifted scholar would shortly arrive. This year, Asher ben Yehiel** had come from west Germany. He was now

---

* Mordecai b. Hillel's life ended in tragedy. On August 12, 1298, in the city of Nuremberg in Germany, he and his wife Selda and their five children died as martyrs.

** Asher ben Yehiel (born 1250, Germany; died Toledo, Spain, 1328). Became one of the most prominent disciples of R. Meir.

a settled member of the household. On this day, as R. Meir was absorbed in dictating his new poem to Rebecca, Joel, her little son, came running into the room, interrupting his grandfather's dication. Asher ben Yehiel appeared on the threshold of the room behind him, laughing.

"I tried to hold the little fellow back," he said. "But, Rebecca, he *is* slippery."

"Not slippery." Little Joel glared momentarily at his friend Asher. "My Mama wants to see me. So does my grandfather."

He ran in screaming delight to his grandfather, who rose as he swung the child up from the floor, holding him high in the air, laughing with him.

"Who says I want to see my youngest grandson? Who? Who?"

"I! I! I!" shrieked Joel in ecstasy.

R. Meir brought him down low enough so that he could hug the child to him. "My dear, sweet Joel, you are a mind-reader. I did want to see you. I was dictating a poem to your mother, but while I was thinking of the words, one part of my mind kept saying, 'I'd like nothing better than to see my grandson Joel at this very moment.' Lo! In comes my grandson Joel. And now I am very happy."

Rebecca laughed, rose from her desk, and came towards the father she worshiped and the son she adored. "That is very fine," she said. "You wanted to see your grandson Joel, and your grandson Joel wanted to see you. And now you have seen each other."

Skillfully she disengaged the child from her father's arms, put him down on the floor, then turned him toward the door. "And now it is time for Joel to go and play, and it is time for Grandfather to go back to work. Goodbye, little boy. Goodbye."

The three adults watched the little boy march sturdily away on his fat little legs. When he reached the door, he turned, gave them all an angelic smile, and ran off down the corridor. The three grown-ups smiled at each other a little sheepishly, each feeling it wasn't quite manly to allow a tiny tot to twist their hearts with love so much.

"But he is a sweet one," Asher said defensively.

Rebecca smiled.

"And now I'll take myself off too and stop disturbing you in your work."

Asher turned to the door, but R. Meir stopped him. "Wait, Asher. Sit down a moment." R. Meir waved his hand toward a chair.

Rebecca resumed her seat at the table and took up her quill.

"Rest a few moments, Rebecca dear," R. Meir said. "I want to discuss something with Asher."

Rebecca put down her quill. Asher seated himself. They looked expectantly at R. Meir. But he did not speak immediately. He sat, studying his hands, and from the expression on his face the two watchers knew he was deeply troubled. His lips were set a little tighter and his eyes seemed a bit colder. But no other disfiguring mark crossed his face, nor was his voice, when finally he spoke, much more than a little stern.

"Word comes to me of a terrible shame we are going to have to endure."

Asher ben Yehiel made an impatient motion. "Dear God of the world! What now?" he asked angrily. "Haven't we been enduring enough, with the taxation increasing constantly, so mercilessly we can hardly meet it?"

The movement of R. Meir's shoulder was so slight it was almost not perceptible as a shrug. "Money is nothing," he said. "Now it is our dignity which is at stake. Always it is the principle we must seek. The Jew must always guard his dignity."

"Then what . . . ?"

"You are young, Asher, but perhaps not so young that you have not heard of the Jew's badge?"

"Oh yes." Asher's lip curled. "I have heard of it, of course, but I have never seen one. Have you, my Master?"

R. Meir nodded slowly. "When I was living in France for a time, I saw the Jew's badge, a disgraceful piece of cloth sewn on the clothes of a Jew to mark him so that a Christian should know that this was a human being of a different order."

His voice rose harshly. "But in Germany, we have always been free of that indignity. We have been spared the shame of having to wear a scrap of cloth to mark us off as different from our fellow Germans."

Rebecca said quietly, "I've never understood why the popes have felt that the Jews must be so singled out."

Asher ben Yehiel shrugged. "Because there's no other

way of knowing who's a Jew and who's a Christian. We look the same, we dress the same, we act the same . . ."

"Not all the time, thank God!" Rebecca said.

"No, not all the time," R. Meir said gloomily. "We don't go about burning churches, or murdering people . . . Well, then, the Jew's badge is now coming to Germany!"

"No!" cried Rebecca, jumping to her feet.

"To Germany?" Asher asked dully. "You mean that here in our native land, right here in Germany where I was born, where you were born, where Rebecca was born, in our beloved Germany, the Pope is going to make us wear a badge, to point us up with the finger of scorn?"

R. Meir nodded. "Aided and abetted by Emperor Rudolph."

"Oh, that Rudolph!" Rebecca moaned.

R. Meir said slowly, "There has just convened in Vienna an assembly of churchmen under the leadership of the papal legate Gudeo. They have passed a decree that henceforth every German Jew shall wear a pointed horned hat."

"A pointed horned hat?" Asher whispered.

"*Pileum cornutum.*" R. Meir gave it the Latin term.

"A pointed horned hat," Rebecca whispered. "Oh, no, father, no! I could not bear to see you wear such a . . ."

"I shall never wear it!" R. Meir said. "I shall never wear the horned hat. That ends the matter."

"But the Emperor?" Asher asked sullenly.

"The Emperor?" R. Meir laughed. "Let him impale

himself on the horns of that hat. Now, come, Rebecca, let me dictate the last stanza of my poem."

Rebecca, a dazed look in her eyes, turned to the desk and picked up her quill.

Asher ben Yehiel sat, miserably, his eyes fixed on his teacher's face.

R. Meir's voice rang out confidently, boldly, and with vigor:-

> "Forgive, I beseech Thee,
>   Dishonour; be kind from the heavens of Thee,
>   That Thy loved ones be never ensnared, that
>   Thou bear their iniquity."

10

The Archbishop of Mayence

SERIOUS TROUBLE was looming over the horizon for the Jewish communities of Germany. The Emperor Rudolph's demands on the Jews for more and more money were becoming increasingly harder to meet. And against the advice of R. Meir, the Jews now engaged in an adventure which eventually led to tragedy. They took a wrong turn on the road to peace by backing the cause of an imposter.

Before the election of Rudolph as Emperor of Germany, the period between 1254 when Conrad, the son of Frederick II, died, and 1273, when Rudolph was elected, was called "The Great Interregnum" or "The Age of Faustrecht" (the law of the fist), when might made right and there was no established central authority.

This was a period of great development for the German people. They extended their colonizing activities in the northeast. Their cities grew stronger and more independent. Then in 1273, Rudolph of Hapsburg was elected Emperor.

For the first ten years of his reign, Rudolph was willing to levy the usual taxes on the towns under his control. But, eleven years later, in 1284, he announced a tremendous tax, amounting to one-third of the working capital of the towns.

The people rebelled. They took a great risk and supported an imposter to the throne who called himself Emperor Frederick II. Frederick II first set up his headquarters in the city of Neuss. Shortly afterwards, he moved on to the city of Wetzlar, which agreed to give him asylum and protection. There the pretender was able to hold out for a whole year.

Rudolph had a powerful army, whereas the false Frederick the Second had no army to support him. Rudolph was extremely wealthy, while Frederick had no money. The struggle was unequal, and the impostor himself knew that his chances were very slight. Rudolph knew this, and the people who supported Frederick also knew it.

Instead of taking any action against the rebellion, Rudolph let the city of Wetzlar sit quietly and stew in its own juices for twelve long months. Finally, the authorities gave in and delivered the self-styled emperor into the hands of Rudolph I of Hapsburg. The rebellion was ended. But the affair had just begun—for the Jews.

Rudolph was well aware that many Jews had supported the impostor. He determined that they must be taught a lesson. They must learn that the Jews of Germany do not rebel against their emperor. He set about to punish them in a cunning way.

Instead of sending his armies in to crush the rebellious group, he merely gave license to the fanatic Franciscan and Dominican monks. They took over, encouraging rowdy knights and lawless crusaders to do their will.

When they had finished with their sport, many Jews of Boppart and Mayence lay dead.

It was the spring of 1284.

Early one morning, three horsemen were seen on the road leading into Mayence. They were R. Meir of Rothenburg, his daughter Rebecca, and his friend and companion, Meir Ha-Kohen. They had been riding for three days and three nights. They were dirt-streaked from the dust of the road, weary in their saddles, and grim in their eagerness to reach Mayence as quickly as possible. But they still had three more hours of hard riding before reaching their destination.

R. Meir turned to smile at Rebecca. "You insisted on coming, daughter."

Through her fatigue she managed a laugh. "Lead on, Father," she cried gaily. "I'm still alive."

He turned then to Meir Ha-Kohen, who smiled quickly and said, " 'Whither thou goest . . .' "

R. Meir smiled in gratitude.

Now all three riders looked at one another, and smiled as though in salute. They breathed deeply, tight-

ened their hold on the reins, gently nudged their horses to a trot, and rode on to Mayence.

It was late in the morning when they reined in their tired mounts at the home of R. Meir's uncle, R. Judah b. Moses Ha-Kohen, the Chief Rabbi of Mayence.

He greeted them warmly and happily, but R. Meir almost wept at the change he saw in his old uncle. The once proud scholar was now totally changed; he looked shrunken, beaten in spirit, and sick unto death from the ordeal of the recent tragic events.

He sensed their concern. "No, no," he quickly assured them, "the barbarians did not lay a hand on me. But they burned the synagogue . . . with forty-five people inside . . ."

"But why?" cried Rebecca. "What did the Jews of Mayence ever do to antagonize the monks of Mayence?"

Rabbi Judah shrugged slightly and led his guests into the dining-room. When everyone was seated and lunch was being served, he said to Rebecca,

"I believe the Franciscan and Dominican monks to be insane."

"You let them off too easily," Meir Ha-Kohen growled, "if you excuse them on the grounds of insanity."

Rabbi Judah twisted his hands nervously, tragically. "How else can you explain such murderous action? The monks insist that every German must be a Christian. If he is not willing to live as a Christian, then he must not live."

"And the Jews will not become Christians," Rebecca said firmly.

The old gentleman closed his eyes for a moment, almost in protest against the strength of her voice. He had suffered so much in spirit that he would have liked to bolt his door against any further violence, even the violence of emotion.

"These fanatical monks," his gentle voice took up his interrupted recital, "find it easy to inflame the ignorant mobs."

To R. Meir all of this was an old story. In his mind's eye he saw again the burning of the Talmuds in Paris, and the blazing hatred on the face of Nicholas Donin. He remembered something else which he had not thought of for many long years, his talk in the garden with Werner of Mayence. For a moment, lost in thought, once again he pondered the old mystery—who was Werner? Werner of Mayence.

The others continued talking, not noticing R. Meir's preoccupation with his own thoughts. Suddenly his uncle said something to catch his attention:

"The Emperor would have destroyed us all, every Jew, every man, woman and child in Mayence, if it had not been for the intervention of our Archbishop."

"Yes?" R. Meir laughed harshly, awakening Rebecca's fear. Her father had a fierce temper when it was aroused by injustice, and that was precisely why she had come with him to Mayence: to help him guard his temper from leading him into personal trouble. So when her father laughed harshly now and said his monosyllabic "Yes," she stiffened herself in alertness.

R. Meir's voice softened a trifle, but it was still scornful. "And what does the Archbishop want? A tax of his own against the Jews in return for his protection?"

Rabbi Judah shook his head, but R. Meir continued.

"Hand in hand with Rudolph, and he doesn't want to bleed the Jews white? I'll believe that, dear uncle, when I hear your precious Archbishop say it with his own mouth."

Rabbi Judah sighed. "I do not know, my dear nephew, what it is that the Archbishop will say to you. But speak to you he will. At dawn this morning his messenger came requesting your appearance at his castle at four o'clock this very afternoon."

"I don't want to see him," R. Meir said, getting up from the table in his impatience. "I will see the Emperor. And only the Emperor."

Now for the first time Rabbi Judah permitted himself the luxury of a smile. "Calm yourself, dear Meir. The Emperor does not want to see *you*. I would really think he is afraid of you—if I didn't know that he is the Emperor—"

"This is not the first time he has avoided giving me an audience," R. Meir said angrily.

And now Rabbi Judah chuckled. "It is almost a court joke, Meir, that the one Jew he doesn't want to lock horns with is Meir of Rothenburg."

R. Meir shrugged. "So he shunts me off onto one of his archbishops."

Rabbi Judah held up his hand. "No, no, Meir. Don't think slightingly of Archbishop d'Eppenstein. He is a fair man, giving full justice to the Jews. You will find he is our friend—"

"Why?" R. Meir interrupted. "What does he want?"

"Just our friendship," Rabbi Judah said quietly.

R. Meir choked back the retort that his uncle's seemingly naive statement aroused. Instead, he said quietly, "Very well. I shall see him at four."

Promptly at four o'clock, R. Meir appeared at the Archbishop's castle, still accompanied by his daughter and Meir Ha-Kohen. Anger at the Emperor's refusal to deal with him flamed in R. Meir's eyes, and fury at the certain rejection of justice.

He strode into the audience chamber, which was dimly lit in the late afternoon. He saw a figure dressed in the robes of a cardinal, seated very still on a throne-like chair, silently observing his entrance into the room. Anger deepened in R. Meir, and he quickened his stride. When he reached the Archbishop, he bowed his head with barely a hint of movement, and said stiffly,

"Your Eminence."

"Welcome, Meir of Worms."

The voice was low-pitched, cultured, and gentle—and R. Meir was confounded. A trick of the mind—and he was seated in a garden in Paris, listening to Werner of Mayence—

"Werner!" he exclaimed.

The man on the throne laughed softly, rose and came to R. Meir. The two men threw their arms around each other, both talking at once. Rebecca and Meir Ha-Kohen looked at each other with raised eyebrows.

In a few minutes the two older men had recovered themselves sufficiently to remember the two younger people.

Archbishop Werner d'Eppenstein took Rebecca's hand in his; his laughing eyes probed her face, and his deep voice paid her compliments. "A beauty, Meir of Worms. Your daughter is a beauty!"

Later, in telling her mother and Deborah of this meeting with the Archbishop, Rebecca said,

"During the entire time we were there, well over two hours, mind you, he never addressed Father as anything but Meir of Worms."

"Because that's who he was when I first met him in Paris," the Archbishop explained when he saw Rebecca's bewilderment. "Oh, his anger was beautiful to see! I knew it that night in my garden—I knew to what heights of fame he must scale if only because of his anger at injustice. And I have watched your career, Meir of Worms," he said, turning back to R. Meir. "I have watched your legal battles with our Emperor."

He laughed lightly and said. "You do know, Meir of Worms, that Rudolph does not hate the Jews. Oh no. He loves them. It is just that he is power-hungry. And the Jews are the source of much of his wealth. But you he fears, my friend. You he fears."

"And well he may," growled Meir Ha-Kohen.

The Archbishop dropped his pose of lightness, of easy good humor, and became deadly serious.

"Don't try Rudolph too far, Meir of Worms. Be glad that he did not remain here to confront you. Had he

remained, I could not have helped you. Now that he is gone, I may warn you. And warn you I must. Spirit your uncle away. Rabbi Judah is in danger. The decree for his arrest has been signed."

"Could you not have warned him?" Rebecca asked tensely.

Werner d'Eppenstein shook his head. "He would not flee if I urged him to. He believes he must stay to protect his people. But the people cannot be saved. A new tax on the Jews, a tax that will amount to confiscation of their property, will be announced in one week. If the Jews do not pay the tax, they will be imprisoned."

Rebecca cried out.

The Archbishop smiled gently. "Do not fear, Rebecca. Rudolph will not harm them. He has no designs on their bodies. Only on their properties."

"Then why did he permit the monks to burn the synagogue?" Meir Ha-Kohen cried out. "They knew there were people seeking shelter there against their violence!"

Archbishop Werner sighed as he looked at R. Meir. "Is it our fate, Meir of Worms, to meet only at fires?" Then he turned to the younger Meir. "The Emperor, my friend, says he is outraged at the murderous actions of the monks."

"Let him prove it!" Rebecca cried.

Archbishop Werner smiled, a small and secret smile.

"So he says he will do, dear Rebecca," he said softly. "He says he will punish the murderers of the Jews of Boppard and Mayence."

"And will he?" R. Meir asked, as softly.

Silence hung over the room for a moment, a thick silence filled with the heavy breathing of four unhappy people.

A church bell tolled outside.

The Archbishop rose to light another candle on the table around which they sat. He leaned over the candle-flame toward R. Meir, and the soft blaze lighted up his deep-set, sad eyes.

"The Jews of Mayence will be imprisoned, Meir of Worms, and their property confiscated. So has the Emperor decreed."

Into the candle-light, fluttering the blaze, came the answer of Meir of Rothenburg.

"I shall tell the Jews of Mayence to flee from Germany."

A small smile again touched the lips of the Archbishop of Mayence.

11

The Call to Greatness

"**S**TORM CLOUDS are gathering in Germany," said R. Meir to his disciples, who were seated at a long table in his study.

A large book was open in front of Asher ben Yehiel. Meir Ha-Kohen held a writing board on his lap. Next to Asher sat a newly arrived pupil, Samson b. Zadok.*

To the right of the table, Rebecca sat at her slanted writing desk. She had just completed a letter to Solomon ben Adret in Toledo, and had signed it, as she signed all of her father's letters:-

> "With greetings of peace,
> Meir son of Baruch."

She released the support holding the moveable part of the desk so that it went down flat, put down her quill,

* Samson b. Zadok became a learned talmudist. In his writings he was known later as the "Tashbetz."

and looked over at the four men. They were so used to her presence that they would continue their conversation, no matter how confidential the subject.

She looked at her father and sighed. Suddenly she realized that he had become completely white-haired. She shook her head in surprise. He's only sixty-nine, she thought, but he looks older. And why shouldn't he look older, she thought again, half in anger, half in pride. Everyone depends on him.

Maharam, he was called: our teacher, the rabbi, Rabbi Meir. He was the leader of his people, the father of his generation, and the supreme judge for the Jews of Germany and most of Europe. And all of these responsibilities have made him old, she thought angrily. A saying of one of the old rabbis came to her mind. "Childhood is a garland of roses; old age is a thicket of thorns." Then she shook her head gently as she realized she was exaggerating.

R. Meir had not become old in a worn-out way. He was grave because of his countless responsibilities. He was stern because of his belief in the principles of right and justice. But he was as vigorous at sixty-eight as he had been at forty. He was possessed of a strong body and he had suffered no frailties or serious illness. He came from a long-lived family. His father had died in 1275 at a very, very old age, when R. Meir was sixty years old. R. Meir's mind, if anything, became keener and sharper with the advancing years. Rebecca had to admit that she really had nothing to complain about.

If her father was burdened with many responsibilities, the responsibilities of a great leader, it was because he

was the man called to greatness by his generation. He was
fit for greatness. The times demanded courage; he had
courage. The age demanded clear thinking; he had a
great and creative mind. The era demanded leadership;
he carried his people along with his forceful personality,
his strength of character.

The age demanded a hero; the age and the man met at
the proper moment.

Rebecca's attention was called back to the conversation as Meir Ha-Kohen responded to R. Meir's gloomy
statement.

"Storm clouds, my Master? Storm clouds always
hover over the Jews."

"But sometimes they have blown over without doing
too much damage, Meir," R. Meir said. "As when a tree
is uprooted, or a river floods, and the damage seems
slight enough. But these storm clouds seem to me to be
very black, very black indeed, my friends."

Asher ben Yehiel moved impatiently. He was a young
man, and he had the young man's feeling that the old
look at everything with pessimism.

"We weathered the storm of the shameful Jew's
badge," he said a trifle sharply. "You defied the authorities. You refused to wear that horrible horned hat, and
everyone took courage and followed you."

"The hat," R. Meir said, thrusting his arm out impatiently, as though to push aside something contemptible.
"That was almost child's play compared to what is coming. It is this new decree of Rudolph of Hapsburg; his
decree of *servi camerae*."

Servi camerae, thought Rebecca—the decree which

means that the person and property of the Jew become the possession of the king. It was absolute enslavement . . .

"*Servi camerae?*" repeated Samson b. Zadok unbelievingly.

"*Kammerknechtschaft,*" R. Meir gave it its German name.

"You say 'new decree,' my Master," Asher objected. "But is it new? Wasn't it first pronounced by Frederick I . . ."

"Yes, yes," R. Meir interrupted. "In 1157 when Frederick I ratified the charter given to the Jews of Worms by Henry IV in 1090. I know the dates. You know the dates. And you know that he confirmed the privileges of the Jew '*cum ad cameram nostram attineant.*' As literal slaves. Henry IV, Frederick I . . . all the emperors have declared the Jews to be their slaves, *servi camerae.* But . . . Rudolph of Hapsburg means it. He is the first who declares himself ready to enforce that decree."

Silence fell on the room. Into R. Meir's eyes had come the withdrawn look they all recognized. It signaled his complete concentration which could not be disturbed. His pupils, his friends and his family all knew that look. They never knew, however, what thought could start that withdrawal into his mind, a withdrawal so absolute that nothing could touch him at those moments.

They would have been surprised to know that now his thoughts were self-centered: he was berating himself. Guilt feelings swept over him. He felt that, somehow, everything that was happening now was his fault. He had once blamed his teacher Yehiel in Paris because when he had excommunicated Nicholas Donin, he had started a chain of tragic and dramatic events that had brought torture and suffering to the Jews. And Meir had always felt, somehow, guiltily, secretly, that some small measure of blame for these occurrences was Yehiel's.

Then was not a large measure of blame now his? Should he not have been able to battle and defeat Rudolph, Emperor though he was, to a standstill on this *servi camerae* decree? Somehow it was his duty. And somehow he must accomplish this one thing if his life was to have any meaning.

He blinked his eyes, and at this sign, Meir Ha-Kohen quickly interrupted his musings. "Has any action been taken yet?"

R. Meir nodded gloomily. "A new tax—one-third of our working capital."

Asher jumped to his feet. "One-third of our capital! But . . . but that is confiscation!"

Yes, confiscation, R. Meir thought. It was what Werner of Mayence had told him. He should have listened more carefully to the Archbishop d'Eppenstein that day in his castle. The Archbishop was a strong friend of the Jews, but not strong enough to oppose Rudolph the First for their sakes. What had happened to the Jews of Boppard and Mayence would now happen to the rest of the Jews of Germany.

R. Meir squared his shoulders and spoke out in a confident voice. "Confiscation, yes. But we will not pay it."

"Why, my Master?" asked Meir Ha-Kohen. "We have paid taxes as high as these before now. Why not now?"

"The German communities have never paid their taxes to the king collectively," answered R. Meir.

"But the responsum of Rabbi Abigdor . . ." Meir Ha-Kohen started to say.

"The responsum of Rabbi Abigdor ben Elijah Ha-Kohen," interrupted R. Meir, "concerned the Jews of Bohemia. The people of Bohemia pay a collective tax to the king. In Germany we have never done this. Moreover, in this case the *Kammerknechtschaft* clause is most important. If we pay this tax, Rudolph will claim that by doing so we have agreed to become his slaves as well! We have always been self-reliant and independent and free, serving no man, only God. We shall remain courageous and free and independent. The communities will refuse to pay this tax!"

"That is why my brother has come!" Asher said, jumping to his feet again.

But R. Meir impatiently motioned to him to resume his seat.

"Your brother Hayyim* has come from the community of Cologne to seek my opinion. The Jews are bitter about this decree. They have always considered themselves free men, free to own property. The government has always officially recognized their free status. Rebecca," R. Meir said, turning to his daughter, "read that part from my letter to the community of Cologne."

* Hayyim ben Yehiel Hefez Zahab, brother of Asher ben Yehiel, a famous talmudist. Many of his responsa have been printed in the col-

The Call to Greatness

Rebecca leaned over her desk, searched for the proper parchment, and then read the passage aloud, in a voice as ringing and as confident as her father's:-

"For Jews are not subjugated to their overlords as the Gentiles are, in the sense that they have to pay taxes to a particular overlord when they do not live in his domain. The status of the Jew in this land is that of a free land-owner who lost his land but did not lose his personal liberty. This definition of the status of the Jew is followed by the government in its customary relations with the Jews."

When Rebecca's voice stopped, there was a moment of silence.

Then R. Meir's deep voice rang out. "We will not be slaves!"

"But what, what will the people do?" Samson b. Zadok asked despairingly.

"They are already doing it," R. Meir said quietly. "They are beginning to leave Germany."

Leave Germany, Rebecca thought, in sudden panic. Germany is our country. This is our home . . . This is where we were born . . .

"They began leaving some time ago," R. Meir said. "I advised the Jews of Mayence to leave. Rudolph declared his decree of *servi camerae* on the Jews of Mayence last year, and from that moment, Jews began to leave Germany."

---

lections of Responsa by R. Meir of Rothenburg. He often acted as an agent for the community of Cologne. He later played an important part in R. Meir's life. See Chapter 16.

"On your advice?" whispered Samson b. Zadok.

"On my advice," R. Meir said firmly. "The Jews are beginning to leave . . . from Mayence, Speyer, Worms, and Oppenheim. Hundreds of families are on the move. The Jews are leaving Germany."

"But where are they going?" Samson b. Zadok asked.

"To Palestine."

"Palestine!" exclaimed Asher. "What good is that? Palestine is impoverished . . ."

"True, it is an impoverished country," said R. Meir. "More righteousness is required of all who live in the Holy Land, and because of the lack of righteousness, the country is now desolate. Therefore whoever goes there must go with the firm resolve to obey all the commandments and to be righteous. He who goes there in the name of Heaven must plan to conduct himself in sanctity and purity. There is no limit to his reward, provided he can maintain himself there."

Asher fidgeted, and R. Meir permitted a smile to lighten his eyes. "Asher is working up his courage to say something impudent."

The others laughed. Asher blushed, and then nodded.

"It is impudent, my Teacher, so forgive me in advance. I have listened respectfully, as always. You say that if a man lives righteously, he can live in security in Palestine. But, my Master, these people who are going now . . ." He paused, shook his head, and evidently changed his mind. When he continued speaking, he said, "These people who are now going to Palestine, will they find a friendly reception?"

R. Meir nodded. "Word has come to us that the Mongolian khan Argun is now in power. His chief minister is a Jew, Sa'd al-Daulah. Because of Sa'd al-Daulah, the khan has become hospitable to the Jews. They are emigrating to Palestine by the hundreds."

"What will you do?" Asher turned suddenly to Meir Ha-Kohen.

"I?" Meir looked at his younger colleague in surprise. Then he said sternly, "I? I remain with my Master. Whatever R. Meir does, Meir Ha-Kohen will do."

Rebecca smiled to herself. Dear Meir Ha-Kohen, with whom she had carried on that foolish, secret warfare for so long. Meir Ha-Kohen had always said he would never leave his teacher. And now he was promising again. He would never have had to rededicate himself if Asher had not asked the question. But Asher had asked, and Meir Ha-Kohen had said unhesitatingly, "Whatever R. Meir does, Meir Ha-Kohen will do."

Asher turned to R. Meir. "And my teacher . . . what will my teacher do?"

R. Meir looked calmly at Asher, and spoke quietly. "I shall remain in Germany."

Everyone present nodded. It was the decision they expected.

Now R. Meir indicated that he wished to be alone. They all left the room. Only Rebecca remained.

R. Meir said gently, "Do you approve my decision, my daughter?"

"Oh yes, Father, yes. But—oh Father—it is a decision to weep about! Our Germany—our people leaving—oh, it is a matter for weeping. Oh Father, I wish I were a little girl again. I could ask you to tell me a story to comfort me."

R. Meir smiled wistfully. "I can tell you a story, a story that will bring you the comfort of tears. Listen, my daughter.

"When Adam and Eve were banished from Paradise, God saw that their grief was heavy and He took compassion on them. He knew the trials and tribulations they would have to face. So, from His treasure-house, He gave them a wondrous treasure. He gave them 'the Tear.' And He said, 'When danger threatens, and your lot is bitter, and you are full of sorrow, tears will run from your eyes and the burden will become lighter and you will have relief.' Man always finds his comfort in this great treasure which God bestowed, my daughter, for, the rabbis say, 'The gates of tears are never shut.' So weep for our people, my daughter. Weep for our country."

12

Decision

THE FAMILY of R. Meir applauded his decision. They would remain in Germany. They would not surrender. They would resist Rudolph of Hapsburg.

Life in the stone house in Rothenburg on the Tauber remained the same except that Asher ben Yehiel was gone. He had married and had two sons by now and had settled in a town in northern Germany.

Sarah continued to supervise the housekeeping of the large establishment, assisted chiefly by Deborah, and to grow prize flowers in her beautiful rose-garden. Deborah's husband, Moses ben Simon, and Rebecca's husband, Solomon ben Isaac, continued in their businesses without interference. Rebecca and Meir Ha-Kohen wrote, as usual, R. Meir's responsa, his answers to legal queries which still came to him from all over Europe. R. Meir continued to work on his tosafot, his notes to the Talmud.

Outwardly, life seemed the same. Everyone went about his work, as busy as always. If anything, they were even busier than before because of the added tensions which kept mounting. For three years these tensions had been building up. New stories of atrocities came to them almost every week.

Under the rule of Rudolph a new hatred was unleashed, and it found its object in the persecution of the Jews. For a long time the Jews in Germany had lived in comparative friendship with their Christian neighbors. But when the Jews resisted Rudolph's desire to enslave them by his *servi camerae* decree, he determined to beat them to their knees.

When a blood-thirsty monk incited his people to murder the Jews, Rudolph closed his eyes or looked the other way. When the Jews of Mayence complained about the murder of the forty-five innocent Jews, the Emperor pretended to listen, gravely, to the case—and then released the murderers without penalty. Life for the Jew of Germany became terror-ridden.

Each week, each month, new and terrible stories came to R. Meir, who was trying to save his people from the shame of slavery.

In Munich, a synagogue was burned with one hundred and eighty people inside. In Oberwesel and Boppard, Jews were murdered in cold blood.

For three years these atrocities mounted. But R. Meir

never wavered in his determination to remain in Rothenburg and to attempt to fight the evil conditions.

One day, Hayyim b. Yehiel, Asher's brother, came to the stone house unexpectedly. Everyone gathered in R. Meir's study to welcome him, wondering what bad news he had brought.

Rebecca, standing behind her mother's chair, saw with one look at Hayyim's white face that the news was very, very bad.

R. Meir was not in a hurry to hear the news. He had listened to nothing but sad, miserable stories for so long, that for this one moment his courage left him. He would willingly have sent Hayyim on his way without hearing what he had come to say. He permitted the women-folk to ask the usual family questions of Hayyim: they enquired after his health, his family, his children, and his business.

Everyone seemed compelled to keep talking about every-day, insignificant things, as if they had entered into a conspiracy to keep Hayyim quiet about anything but the most trivial matters.

But eventually R. Meir's weak moment left and his courage returned. He made a slight movement with his right hand and everyone fell silent. Meir Ha-Kohen stiffened in his chair. Samson b. Zadok sat up straight. Deborah reached over to take her mother's hand. And Rebecca went to stand behind her father. Hayyim dropped his eyes to the floor, and kept wetting his lips.

"Hayyim," R. Meir said quietly.

Hayyim sighed deeply. He raised his eyes. "Friend,

teacher . . ." He stammered. "It is my brother. Asher. Asher has been driven from his home . . ."

"Asher!" breathed Rebecca.

"He and his children have been driven out of Germany with only the clothes they wore on their backs."

"Was he hurt?" R. Meir asked.

Hayyim raised his right shoulder slightly. "A little. Not too badly. But he has left everything behind. He has had to flee to the south of France without a penny. He must begin his life as a beggar."*

The family began to question Hayyim, but R. Meir kept silent, his eyes resting on, without seeing, the manuscript on Rebecca's slant board. He was deep in thought, concentrating so completely that he did not even hear the buzz of conversation going on about him.

After a little while he raised his head, and spoke.

"Rebecca, is Solomon coming home for dinner at twelve o'clock?"

"Why, of course, Father. Solomon comes home every day."

"Deborah, will Moses be here also?"

"Yes, Father."

"Good." R. Meir rose. "After dinner has been eaten, we will remain for a talk. Hayyim, you will honor us, please, by remaining."

"Thank you, Rabbi Meir."

The large meal of the day was eaten at noon, and

* Asher ben Yehiel, forced to flee from Germany, went first to South France, then to Toledo, Spain. Wherever he went, he continued to write; but he lived out his life in extreme poverty.

usually Sarah and Deborah had no complaints about their food being appreciated. R. Meir's family and his students enjoyed the delicious food that Sarah set before them, the gracious companionship and relaxation of the meal, and the table-songs after grace was recited.

But today no one had much appetite either for food or conversation, and R. Meir led them quickly into grace after meals. The entire family was present: R. Meir and his wife, Rebecca and Deborah and their husbands and children who now were grown.

R. Meir wasted no time in preliminaries. He plunged into the heart of the matter. "The troubles that have been brewing in our country are beginning to creep closer. The news Hayyim brings us of our beloved Asher spells out for us how close to home the danger comes. Our moment of decision has come."

R. Meir paused.

And Meir Ha-Kohen said, "But still there is one more bit of news, my Master. The letter you received today?"

R. Meir turned his searching eyes on Meir Ha-Kohen. He nodded, and speaking clearly, said, "Today, a letter written by Rudolph the Emperor, has come to my hand. This is what the letter says:-

"Since the person and property of the Jews as a group, and every individual Jew, belong to the king, and since a number of them have fled without his permission, he shall appropriate the real and personal property they have left behind . . ."

Solomon b. Isaac and Moses b. Simon glanced apprehensively at each other. They were the businessmen of the family, and they knew that this total confiscation meant poverty, hunger, disease and despair.

R. Meir continued. "The Emperor has appointed the Archbishop of Mayence and Count Eberhard of Katzenellenbogen as the trustees over the property left behind by our brethren."

"The Archbishop of Mayence?" interrupted Rebecca. "Werner d'Eppenstein? Our friend?"

"He is our friend, Rebecca," her father said. "You know he will deal as gently with our people as he can. I am glad he is one of the trustees. He has written me in secret that he will deal gently and justly with the Jews."

"He will," Rebecca said quietly. "As far as the Emperor will permit."

"Of course he will," Meir Ha-Kohen said impatiently, irritated with Rebecca for interrupting. Worse and more dreadful news must be told the family, and he wanted them to know quickly and to spring into action even more quickly. So now he turned to R. Meir, and said, "Tell them . . ."

The shake of R. Meir's head was so slight that only Meir Ha-Kohen, for whom it had been intended, observed. R. Meir's voice broke in smoothly to silence Meir Ha-Kohen's revelation, and he said,

"My dear ones, the danger comes closer and closer to home."

Meir Ha-Kohen said softly, "Very close to home." He was about to add, "There is a price on our beloved teacher's head."

But R. Meir warned him sharply, "Meir!"

Decision

Meir Ha-Kohen caught R. Meir's eye. He nodded, closed his mouth, and sighed deeply. Rebecca saw this little by-play, and wondered what it meant. But her father was speaking again.

"My children, today we are faced with a grave decision. For three years we have watched our brethren escaping from Germany by the hundreds. We elected to remain. But in these three years matters have not improved. They have worsened. I believe the time has come for us to re-examine our decision. Do we remain? Or do we go?"

R. Meir stopped talking, but no one spoke up. He had always made every decision for the family. And they had always agreed to what he decided. So they waited for him to continue.

He shook his head. "Speak up. I want to know just how you feel."

"But, Father," Rebecca said. "You know it is for you to decide. You know that if you remain, we remain. If you go, we go."

"But my child, this time it is different. Three years ago when I said we would remain, we were remaining in our own home where we could reasonably expect life to go on as always. Now if I say we shall go, we will be going into exile, into the unknown. Each of you must have the right to decide for himself."

Solomon ben Isaac laughed softly. "My dear Father, all of us sitting at this table are adult, grown up, and capable of making decisions. Each of us may have an opinion as to the wiser course of action. But you know full well, dear Father, that not one of us here will decide in any way contrary to you."

A murmur of voices rose, saying, "Yes, yes," "Of course," "No question."

Solomon ben Isaac looked around at the family, smiling at their murmured agreement. Then he turned back to his father-in-law. "You see, Father? Do you decide to remain? We remain. Do you decide to go? As Ruth of old said, 'Whither thou goest, I will go.'"

R. Meir bowed his head, first because he was overwhelmed by the deep trust and devotion of his children, all grown men and women, waiting for him to make their decision. Secondly, he wanted a moment's more thought to make sure he was deciding correctly, since all of these lives, all of these careers depended on him.

Rebecca looked at her father's bowed head, at the noble head of silken white hair, and she felt a pang in her heart. How difficult it was to be the head of the family; how hard to make the decision.

It wasn't always so hard. She had seen her father make hundreds of decisions. But they were decisions of law, or of justice, dealing with ritual matters, synagogue affairs, business contracts. But this is a different decision, my Father, isn't it, she thought? This is a decision involving the life and death of other individuals, especially those dearest to you. Such decisions are not made easily.

Sarah gazed at her husband's bowed head, and she, too, felt a pang in her heart. The decision was not difficult for her. As long as she had her entire family with her, she would feel only one regret at leaving, a regret at having to give up her garden.

Deborah looked at her father's bent head, and she wept silently for him. The music that was always present in her heart was silent now. He should not have to make such a decision. He is old now, even though he is still strong and his mind is keener than it ever was, but he is bowed down with the weight of years and it should be a younger heart which takes this terrible, terrible weight of guilt. Make *us* decide, she cried silently, make *us* decide.

But R. Meir raised his head, looked at each member of his family with clear, untroubled eyes, and spoke out in a firm voice, unmarred by doubt.

"We shall go," he said.

"No!"

Everyone turned in amazement to Sarah, who had risen quickly and was leaning on the table towards her husband.

"No, Meir, no . . ." She fell silent, bent her head, and thought, it is only my heart that speaks. She raised her head, smiled gently, and said, "Forgive me, my husband." She stood straight. "We shall go."

Deborah wanted to jump up and tell her mother she was right, they must not go, but she, too, thought, it is only my heart that tells me we should stay. My mind tells me that my father knows what is best.

Rebecca smiled confidently at her father.

The silence was broken by Meir Ha-Kohen. "My Master," he said, "Helena and I beg leave to go with you."

"Of course, Meir," R. Meir said quietly. "Of course, Helena. You are part of our family. Whichever one of our friends wishes to travel with us, we shall be glad to have them. It will take us one month to make all our arrangements, to convert some of our holdings into cash, to pack our belongings.

"We shall leave on the first day of April, to cross the Alps into Lombardy."

13

Journey South

PREPARATIONS for depar-
ture from Rothenburg were begun in secrecy. The nobles
of the area must not discover that they were losing their
taxable subjects. They could very well put R. Meir and
his family in prison to keep them from leaving Rothenburg. Arrest and imprisonment would not mean danger,
however, only inconvenience. The nobles were intent
only on safeguarding their property. Money was the most
important single desire of the bishops and the kings. The
Jews were taxable, and the rulers could not lose this
valuable source of income. Therefore they imprisoned
them, if necessary, to retain them for taxation.

To secure their freedom, the Jews had to pay a
ransom—another form of taxation. With the arousal of
Rudolph's greed, this might mean the confiscation of a

man's entire estate. He had meant every word of his decree:-

"I shall appropriate the real and personal property. . ."

Therefore it was vital that R. Meir and his family make their preparations for departure with utmost secrecy. This involved great difficulties. Moses ben Simon, Deborah's husband, was entrusted with the task of obtaining the horses and the wagons. There were to be twenty-nine people in their party, not counting four other families who were traveling with them. The others would provide their own transportation. But for R. Meir's family alone, preparation involved three wagons with two horses for each wagon, and horses for Solomon ben Isaac, Moses ben Simon, and their grown sons and sons-in-law.

R. Meir was to ride in one wagon with Sarah, Rebecca to handle the horses in the second wagon, and Meir Ha-Kohen the third. The other men were to travel on horseback, some guarding the wagons, some riding ahead to search out the friendly stopping-places.

Many inns were owned by Jews, and the travelers would have no difficulty finding resting-places each night. Still, it was important to carry enough food to take care of the party, and particularly for Rebecca's and Deborah's small grandchildren. At the age of seventy, R. Meir had six great-grandchildren.

They planned to gather provisions along the way, but it was wise to stock up on as many staples as they could carry. Solomon ben Isaac, Rebecca's husband, was in charge of securing the provisions.

The women were to pack all clothes and belongings. Rebecca left this task to her mother and sister and the other grown women in the family. She had something more important to do; she went into her father's study to help him pack his books.

He stood with his back to her, his eyes gazing moodily at his desk. Behind him, unnoticed, stood Meir Ha-Kohen, his eyes riveted to the back of his master's head. R. Meir, unaware of their presence, was preoccupied with thoughts that were inexpressibly sad. The time for parting with so many things he had held dear had come. The stone house on the Tauber, in which he had lived for half a century, where his children had been married and his grandchildren and great-grandchildren had been born, where his pupils had come and lived and gone from, pupils, disciples and friends, this house their life— now must be torn away from them.

Here at this desk he had received letters from so many friends and colleagues—R. Kalonymus, R. Hezekiah of Merseburg, R. Shneor, R. Isaac b. Abba Mari of Marseilles. Here he had written to many friends and rabbis —R. Israel b. Urshrago, R. Menahem b. Natronai, R. Jacob of the community of Linpurk. Would he ever receive any more letters? Would R. Yakar Ha-Levi and R. Shemaiah Ha-Kohen know where to write to him? Would he ever write letters again? From where would he write to R. Yekutiel and R. Shemariah?

Would he ever again pick up a book and study?

He sighed, and reached forward to pick up a manuscript. In his movement he caught sight of Meir Ha-Kohen, watching him. He turned and saw Rebecca, watching them both.

He smiled. "Ah, my children. You have caught me indulging in self-pity. That is a luxury we cannot permit ourselves."

"Perhaps." Meir Ha-Kohen came forward. "But when we say goodbye to one way of life, without knowing what is waiting in the new life, we should be permitted the luxury of remembering the life we say farewell to."

R. Meir nodded. "We carry these memories with us, and, with the help of Heaven, we look for the life to be continued in new surroundings. But it is hard, my children, to leave one's country."

"But we go to the Holy Land, Master," Meir Ha-Kohen objected.

"We go to the Holy Land, Meir," R. Meir said, "with great joy. We shall look upon the hills of Judea. We shall stand in Jerusalem where David stood and tread the ground trodden by Isaiah and Jeremiah and all the noble people of Israel. And my heart swells in joyful anticipation. But, still, still it is hard to leave one's home."

"The memories of sun-washed days on the Tauber," whispered Rebecca. "The star-lit nights of Succoth in our garden. Home is where the memories are, Meir."

He made an embarrassed gesture. "Oh, I know, Rebecca, I know. But our memories include Jews burned in synagogues . . ."

"No, Meir," R. Meir stopped him. "Every life has its tragedies. Every life has its grief. And the life of the Jew has known tragedy and grief. But it has also known joy." The old man's voice rang out triumphantly.

"Joy," Meir muttered gloomily. "Without a country... Germany is no motherland. It is a step-motherland."

"Yes, a step-motherland, I agree. But at times the step-mother has been kind. She has permitted us to live here. Here we have worked and raised our families. Here we have created. No, Meir, I will not always weep for the Jew. I will exult for him. Without his own homeland, he has nevertheless created! He has been an example of courage, of the spirit of freedom, of the ideal of the worth of the individual. The Jew is a creator! I will not weep for him!"

Sarah had come to the door unnoticed, and she had heard her husband's joyful hymn of life. The tears streamed down her face. "Good! Oh good!" she cried.

They all whirled to see her. She took a large kerchief from the pocket of her apron and dried her tears.

"My heroic husband. Those are words to inspire any faltering heart. And now, don't you think it's time to pack your books?"

They all laughed, and the solemn moment ended, but the memory of it always lived in each of the four lives.

R. Meir, Rebecca and Meir Ha-Kohen set themselves to the task of packing R. Meir's books. It was a large library, collected over many years, so valuable to him that he felt that if anything happened to it his life would not be worth living. He picked up each book, fondled it,

opened it, and sighed over it before handing it to Meir
Ha-Kohen or Rebecca. And every once in a while he
would murmur,

"Sefer, dear sefer, what is going to happen to you?"

Every man's life is rooted to a particular thing. R.
Meir's was rooted to his manuscripts. As he handled
them now, he was inclined to moodiness and fear.

"I feel as if I am losing my roots," he said. "My precious books are leaving me. I shall lose my library. I
shall lose the breath of my life."

"Father dear," Rebecca said gently. "Your books will
always be with you. You are not sending them away.
Nor are you going away from them. They are going with
you. Wherever you go, your books will be there."

"I hope you are right, my child. But I am weighted
down with a premonition. I feel certain I shall be separated from my books."

Rebecca and Meir Ha-Kohen teased R. Meir, laughing gently at him, trying to jolly him out of his black
mood.

"How often do we have these false premonitions, my
Master," Meir Ha-Kohen said. "Fortunately they are
often false. Come now, my Teacher. We will load your
books into the wagon in which you will travel. You will
be able to keep your eye on them all through the journey."

Thus cajoling, teasing and laughing, they took each
manuscript away from R. Meir as he lingered over it,
and packed it away. Finally, all the books were safely
stowed away.

R. Meir looked at the now empty room. "How quickly a room looks unlived in. I am willing to leave it now. Without my books it is empty of soul. It is easy to turn my back on it." He did so, walked to the door, and over his shoulder, without looking back, said, "Come, Meir. Now we shall help you pack your books."

Meir Ha-Kohen's library was not as extensive as R. Meir's, but it was a fine collection. For some time he had been engaged in writing a legal code and he had gathered a good library of his own.

Two days before they were to leave, R. Meir was looking for his wife. Unable to find her anywhere in the house, he went out into the garden.

There he found her, with Deborah. They were not doing anything. They were just standing quietly, Deborah with her arm around her mother's shoulders, gazing at the garden. It was too early for anything to be in bloom. In that barren time between the end of winter and the beginning of spring, everything looked desolate. But the two women were not seeing it as it looked now. In their mind's eye they were seeing the garden as it would look in full bloom in the summer.

R. Meir felt the weight of their unspoken sorrow. He walked forward slowly and put his arms around them both.

"Do not grieve for the garden you must leave. You will plant other gardens. Only remember that you did create beauty. It will live in your heart. It will live in the hearts of your children and in the hearts of our pupils and our friends who were refreshed by that beauty."

Journey South

By the night of April first, all the work was done. Moses had the horses. Solomon had the provisions. All possessions were packed and stored and ready. The last meal was eaten out in Sarah's garden, even though the air was raw, and a strong wind blew. One last meal in Mother's garden.

The songs after dinner were few, but they were sung lustily. R. Meir set the mood of holiday-making for the family. There was to be no gloom; joy must reign. The little children especially were infected by their great-grandfather's high spirits, and their tiny, treble voices rang out clearly, although not always true to pitch.

It was only later, when they had retired early, that each grownup let the smile fade from his lips and felt his heart grow heavy with the grief of leaving his home. Many a pillow smothered a sob, and many a pillow was stained with tears.

But just before dawn, when everyone rose to prepare for departure, there were no signs of tears and no sighing or sobbing.

They must be on the road before the sun rose. There was no time for anything but sharp action. The morning air was chill, and damp with heavy dew. Each person dressed warmly and ate a hot, sustaining breakfast.

R. Meir was the first person to walk out of the stone house in the walled city of Rothenburg on the river Tauber. He walked out with a steady step, his head held high. The family followed him. Whither away? To what future? To what fortune? It was in the hands of Heaven. Heaven would lead the way.

R. Meir's wagon was the first to start. In a clear, ringing voice, he called out, "Farewell to the Tauber! Forward to the future!"

The little children picked up the cry: "Forward! Forward!"

Rebecca's two grown sons, David and Joel, and Deborah's son Judah, already mounted on their horses, now set out at a gallop and quickly pulled away from the party. The road ahead held many unknown dangers. They would have to travel through woods and forest. Robbers and thieves lurked amongst the trees. Occasionally, a traveler might meet a lone Crusader, returned from the last Crusade to the Holy Land, where he had shed blood and had seen blood shed; he would not hesitate to shed more blood to obtain booty as rich as this caravan must possess. Or a traveler might meet a dozen or so farmers readying themselves to join a new crusade to the Holy Land. They were prepared to kill infidels, and if they met any people on the highway whom they could consider infidels, the looting and burning and murdering could just as well begin at home.

Therefore David and Joel and Judah rode on ahead to scout out the land.

At the rear of the caravan, mounted on strong horses, rode Rebecca's and Deborah's sons-in-law, prepared to defend the caravan against a surprise attack at the rear.

Leading the caravan, keeping pace with the horses pulling the heavily ladened wagons, were Moses ben Simon and Solomon ben Isaac.

Moses and Solomon had mapped out a plan of travel. Their road would lead them up the river Rhine, across the Alps and into Italy, to the region of the Lombards. They hoped to reach Lombardy by the second week in June.

In Italy, in the city of Rome, the Bishop of Basle was making his preparations to travel back from Rome to his home in Basle. He planned to travel northward from Rome to the Lombard country, across the Alps and down the Rhine.

Traveling from Italy to Switzerland was just as hazardous as traveling from Rothenburg to Italy. The Bishop had collected a bodyguard of eight soldiers, and his secretary, Kneppe, to travel with him.

Kneppe had been born a Jew. But he had decided five years before that he would rather be a Christian. He had converted, and because of his shrewdness he had managed to insinuate himself into the company of the Bishop of Basle. The Bishop was willing enough to convert Jews to Christianity, but he did not fully trust the converts. A man who can betray one side, he felt, can betray the other just as easily.

The Bishop felt there was something sly about Kneppe; he was too amiable and ready, and too obsequious. But although he disliked the man, he could find no other suitable secretary to accompany him, and so he engaged him, intending to discharge him as soon as they reached Basle.

Kneppe, however, did not perceive that the Bishop

disliked him. He fawned upon the prelate and was sure that the Bishop must regard him highly. Just to play safe, however, he decided to keep his eyes open for any opportunity to show the Bishop what a really good Christian he had become.

The Bishop's party set out from Rome.

R. Meir's party stopped at the inn of Abraham b. Ruven on the outskirts of the city of Gorz, Germany, on the morning of June 22, 1286.

The Bishop of Basle's party arrived at the inn of Abraham b. Ruven on the outskirts of the city of Gorz on the morning of June 28, 1286.

14

Treachery

THE BISHOP gave the command to stop.

"Kneppe," he ordered. "Arrange for the quartering of the horses and the men. We will remain here for three days."

"But, Your Eminence," Kneppe protested. "This inn is owned by a Jew."

The Bishop looked at him coldly. "So much the better. Then we know the food will not be poisonous. We know we shall not be assaulted and robbed. With Jews we shall be safe."

With a contemptuous flick of his whip, which came dangerously close to Kneppe's nose, the Bishop turned his back on him, dismounted, threw the reins of his horse towards his groom's waiting hands, and set off down the road for a walk to ease his saddle-strained muscles.

Kneppe avoided the eye of the smirking groom, and started towards the main house. The soldiers dismounted and stood at ease beside their horses, waiting for orders.

Kneppe stepped smartly. He must have everything arranged before the Bishop returned. The Bishop would expect all arrangements to be made quickly, and perfectly, and he desired to please the Bishop.

He saw three wagons near the stables and several black horses. The equipment looked so fine that he decided it must belong to a bishop or a cardinal. But when he hurried inside and saw the crowd of people there, he could find no mitres or scarlet hats to indicate the presence of any high churchmen.

Near the fireplace was a large group of people. There were tall, strong men standing there, and young children playing on the floor, watched over by pretty, young women; three older women were seated. In the heart of the group sat an old man with white hair.

Kneppe was torn by a desire to study this group, to find out who these people were, and whether he could gain any advantage from them. But he had to hurry and make the arrangements before the Bishop arrived. Reluctantly, he went to find the landlord.

Abraham b. Ruven, the landlord, was a tall, heavy-set, black-haired man, with piercing brown eyes and a square jaw. It was no easy task, especially for a Jew, to operate an inn on the main highway to the city of Gorz. Along this road came travelers of all kinds, trustworthy and untrustworthy men, knaves out to rob anyone they could, and crusaders always bent on trouble. The landlord of an inn needed to be bold, strong and brave.

Abraham b. Ruven was such a man. He had learned to size up a man quickly and well. Now, as Kneppe came hurrying towards him, his eye roving back to the group near the fireplace, Abraham characterized him in his mind. A rogue, he thought. Ready for deceitful schemes. Cruel. Dangerous. It was on the tip of his tongue to turn the man away with, "Sorry. There is no room in the inn."

But Kneppe was faster. Smiling ingratiatingly, he said, "My Master, the Bishop of Basle . . ."

Abraham had no special love for these so-called princes of the Church, but he had no cause to antagonize this particular bishop. He *did* have the room, and he *could* quarter the horses.

He and Kneppe were kept busy for the next hour getting everyone and everything settled. The Bishop was pleased with all the arrangements and threw Kneppe a bone.

"Well done, Kneppe. Well done."

"Thank you, m'lord," Kneppe murmured, bending low, looking humble, but cheering inside.

Scored! Scored a bull's-eye, he exulted silently. Satisfied with himself, at leisure now until supper-time, he strolled about ostensibly amusing himself. But he kept trying to get closer to the group near the fireplace. He wanted to see the old man's face. Something was nagging at him, and for some reason he had to see the face of the group's leader.

The white-haired man was R. Meir. He and his family
had arrived safely in Lombardy after a tedious, unevent-
ful journey. It had been a tiring trip. They were all glad
to have a rest here at this fine inn. The innkeeper, Abraham b. Ruven, had given them every comfort, and it
would be pleasant to remain there for a while longer.

But they had already been at Gorz for six days. It was
time to push on further. They planned to remain one
more day and to leave before dawn on the morning of
June 29th.

Just before supper, R. Meir walked out into the garden with his two sons-in-law and Meir Ha-Kohen to discuss their plans for departure on the day after the
morrow. Kneppe was hanging about, waiting for an
opportunity to see the elderly man of the group. When
he saw R. Meir leave the inn by one door, he left by the
other and sauntered around to make it look as if he were
just out for a stroll.

In a few moments he came face to face with R. Meir.
He nodded his head in greeting. The four men greeted
him as silently, without breaking the rhythm of their
step.

Kneppe walked on slowly until he was around the side
of the house, out of their sight. Then he broke into a run
until he reached the door. He hurried into the house,
going so fast that he almost collided with the innkeeper,
Abraham, who was talking to Joel, Rebecca's son. He
apologized and hurried past them towards the stairs.

Abraham looked after him until he was out of sight.
Then in a low voice he said to Joel, "I don't like the

look of that man. He looks like a wrong one. I think he's
a Jew."

"Traveling with a Bishop?" Joel's voice expressed dis-
belief.

"A converted Jew," Abraham grumbled. "And they're
not to be trusted. I wonder what he's up to."

"Nothing, probably," Joel answered. "You're letting
your imagination run away with you, Mr. Landlord."

Abraham rubbed his hand along the side of his face,
his eyes still on the stairway up which Kneppe had
gone.

"Perhaps," he admitted, but doubtfully. "I'd still like
to know what he's doing."

At that moment Kneppe was knocking on the Bishop's door. After a moment he heard the key turn in the
lock, and the door opened.

When the Bishop saw who was standing there, he
frowned. "Why do you disturb me before my evening
meal?"

Kneppe was breathing heavily, as much from his excitement at what he had discovered as from having run
all the way.

"Your Eminence, it is of the greatest import!"

"Then tell me quickly."

Kneppe looked back over his shoulder. He whispered,
"If I may enter . . . Your Eminence . . . perhaps it would
be wiser."

The Bishop's frown deepened. With a gesture of dis-
taste, he opened the door a few inches, barely enough
for Kneppe to squeeze through. The Bishop closed the

door, moved two steps away and turned to look at his secretary. Kneppe leaned away from the door, and whispered.

"Your Eminence, in that large group of guests . . . in that group . . ." He paused.

The Bishop wanted to reach forward and shake this oily devil. He controlled himself.

"Speak up, you fool."

"The leader of that group," Kneppe spoke slowly, as if savoring his news. "The leader is Rabbi Meir ben Baruch of Rothenburg!"

"Rabbi Meir ben Baruch of Rothenburg!" The Bishop took two steps forward, grasped Kneppe's arm, and shook him. "Are you certain? Are you sure?"

Kneppe, his eyes glistening with excitement, smirked. "I am certain!"

The Bishop released Kneppe's arm, took a step backward, and let out a long breath. "Ah! Rabbi Meir of Rothenburg." A smile of condescension crossed his face. "Good, my dear Kneppe. Good."

Kneppe bowed, keeping his face impassive. His heart was singing. He didn't see the sneer on the Bishop's face.

"You will have your supper at once, and quickly," the Bishop ordered. "Then you will take two soldiers with you. Ride to the castle of the lord of this city, Count Meinhard. Acquaint him with this fact, and then return with him immediately."

R. Meir and his family sat down to their evening meal, looking forward to the supper with enjoyment.

They were relaxed. They had this evening for rest, to-morrow for preparation, and then they would be back on the highway for the next lap of their journey.

After supper they retired early.

Only the Bishop of Basle was left in the large commons room downstairs. The landlord, Abraham b. Ruven, eyed him sourly. If his Eminence would deign to retire, then he, Abraham, could lock up and go to sleep.

But half past nine came and went, and the Bishop sat on. The hands of the clock moved to nine forty-five, and still the Bishop remained in his chair. The minute hand crept up and up, and then it was ten o'clock.

On the stroke of ten, the front door burst open and in strode Count Meinhard, the lord of the city of Gorz. Behind him came Kneppe, and behind him four of the Count's soldiers.

Abraham hurried forward. "My lord . . ."

But Count Meinhard pushed him aside and strode up to the Bishop, who rose to greet him.

Their excitement was evident only in their failure of manners. They forgot to ask after each other's health, and to put other such polite questions.

"A wonderful stroke of luck!" Count Meinhard said. "The Emperor Rudolph will be pleased."

The Bishop permitted himself to smile. "The biggest plum that could be dropped in his lap."

"A plum indeed!" Count Meinhard smiled and began pulling off his riding gauntlets. He said over his shoulder carelessly, "Abraham, wine for the Bishop and me."

He seated himself next to the Bishop. Kneppe was not invited to sit down. He remained standing near the doorway, where he could be seen if needed and out of the way if not.

"How did you know who it was?" Count Meinhard dropped his gloves onto the table.

"My secretary recognized him." The Bishop openly sneered. "A converted Jew. Leave it to one Jew to recognize another."

Count Meinhard laughed, loudly and harshly.

Kneppe pretended not to have heard.

Abraham, his face stony and white, came through the doorway, jostling Kneppe aside. He would have run and warned R. Meir, but there was no time, and no hope. He could hardly get dressed and away from the inn before they discovered his absence. No hope. As he set the wine glasses before the Count and the Bishop, the Count said,

"My soldiers are surrounding the inn."

Abraham's hand shook as he opened the wine bottle, but he steadied it as he poured a few drops into the Count's glass. The Count raised the glass, sipped the wine, and indicated with a wave of his long fingers that it was satisfactory. Abraham filled the Bishop's glass, then the Count's. He set the bottle of wine on the table between them.

Kneppe was not offered any wine.

Before Abraham could turn away, the Count said, "My good Abraham. You are to go upstairs to your guest, Rabbi Meir of Rothenburg. Inform him that

Count Meinhard, lord of Gorz, requires his presence below."

Abraham turned away.

The Count added, "Immediately."

Abraham paused. He knew the Count well. He was usually a pleasant, friendly, easy-going man. Perhaps . . . Abraham turned back.

"My lord, the Rabbi has retired for the night. He is not a young man. Perhaps . . ."

The Count's voice flicked out at him like a whiplash. "Abraham. Immediately."

"Yes, my lord." Abraham bowed slightly, turned, started for the door.

Count Meinhard's voice rang out.

"Luigi!"

One of the soldiers stepped to the door and snapped to attention.

"Accompany our good host Abraham."

Abraham reached Kneppe. He stopped. He gave him a look so filled with burning hatred that Kneppe involuntarily drew back. The landlord walked on through the doorway and turned to the stairs. The soldier was at his side.

It wasn't necessary for Abraham to knock as loudly as he did, nor to shout at R. Meir's door. But he did. He pounded on the door. And he shouted—purposely, so that Solomon b. Isaac and Moses b. Simon and Meir Ha-Kohen would hear also, because with the soldier at his side the innkeeper could not give them any other warning.

He pounded on the door and he shouted, "Rabbi Meir! Rabbi Meir! Wake up! Wake up, Rabbi Meir!"

Immediately, every door opened, and when R. Meir's door opened, Abraham spoke in a loud voice so everyone in his family could hear.

"Rabbi Meir, the lord of the city of Gorz is belowstairs. Count Meinhard requests your presence, Rabbi Meir. You are to come immediately."

R. Meir saw the soldier standing behind the innkeeper. Quietly he said, "Trouble?"

Abraham nodded. Loudly he said, "You are to come immediately."

"Give me a moment to dress." R. Meir closed the door.

Abraham stood motionless, looking at the closed door. He felt his heart was breaking. He wanted to weep bitter tears. He wanted to smash something—to break the door down with his hands.

The soldier stood motionless. He looked at the back of Abraham's neck and watched it turn red, then white, then red again.

Somewhere nearby came the sound of a woman weeping.

R. Meir's door opened. R. Meir stood there, fully clothed; then he stepped out. Turning to Sarah, who stood white-faced at the door, he smiled gently, then pulled the door closed.

Other doors opened. From them came Solomon ben Isaac, Moses ben Simon, David ben Solomon, Joel ben Solomon, Judah ben Moses, and Meir Ha-Kohen. They fell into step and marched down the hallway until they surrounded R. Meir b. Baruch.

Then, altogether, they started for the stairway, followed by Abraham, their host, and the soldier of Gorz. They walked steadily, with unfaltering step, to the door of the commons room. At the door of the commons room, R. Meir levelled one terrible glance at Kneppe. Kneppe turned white and put his hand to his throat.

R. Meir turned his face away from the traitor.

He marched forward, his sons-in-law, his grandsons, and Meir Ha-Kohen walking behind him. The Bishop watched him approach, thinking—what a superb old man—what courage, what nobility!

R. Meir stopped in front of Count Meinhard. "Your lordship wishes to see me?"

The Bishop rose. Count Meinhard rose. His eyes rested for a moment on the face of this most famous of scholars. When he spoke, it was respectfully, but firmly.

"Rabbi Meir ben Baruch of Rothenburg?"

"I am he, Meir ben Baruch of Rothenburg."

Count Meinhard gave a flick of his fingers as a salute, and said, "Rabbi Meir ben Baruch of Rothenburg, I arrest you, in the name of the Emperor, Rudolph the First of Hapsburg!"

15

The Castle at Wasserburg

"**A**RREST?" With one voice, the men of R. Meir's family cried out the word.

R. Meir stood impassive. This came as no shock to him, although it was the realization of his deepest fears. Rudolph I of Hapsburg was serious in his intention to squeeze every penny he could out of his subjects; he would not let them get out of his reach. Meir of Rothenburg was his most serious enemy, and he would do anything to prevent his escape.

R. Meir's arrest was a master-stroke for the Emperor.

Shock and surprise numbed the other men until Count Meinhard made an impatient gesture with his fingers. Then Solomon b. Isaac's tongue was loosened.

"You cannot arrest him! He has done nothing criminal. He is the leader of the Jews . . ."

A mocking smile spread over the Count's face. R. Meir observed it, and saw the cold look in his eye. Without turning, still facing the Count, he raised his right hand to silence Solomon b. Isaac. "Solomon, my son."

Solomon, fuming, controlled himself with a supreme effort.

R. Meir turned to face his children. Looking with grief at their white, drawn faces, he felt an urgent need to console them, to reassure them. He smiled gently, and said in a clear voice, "My sons, a mistake has been made. We shall soon set it right. Just be patient."

He turned again to face the Bishop and Count Meinhard. He bowed his head slightly, and said, "Take me to the Emperor."

Count Meinhard decided on immediate action. He left the inn with his prisoner as the clock struck midnight.

R. Meir was mounted on one of his own black horses, but he did not ride in the midst of the soldiers. Four soldiers rode at the head of the little procession, followed by Count Meinhard, the Bishop of Basle, and Kneppe. Then came R. Meir, protected by his sons-in-law, Solomon b. Isaac and Moses b. Simon, and their sons: David and Joel and Judah, and Meir Ha-Kohen. The rest of the men remained behind to escort the women and children and wagons back to Germany. They were to meet in the city of Wasserburg.

Count Meinhard had sent a scout ahead to Rudolph to tell him he was bringing him a prize prisoner.

Rudolph the First of Hapsburg, Emperor of Germany, was at Wasserburg when they arrived. He stood on the balcony of the Castle overlooking the moat, watching Count Meinhard's party ride through the castle gates, hearing the hooves of the horses clattering on the rough cobblestones. And Rudolph smiled.

Count Meinhard looked up and saw him. He raised his sword in salute. Rudolph raised his arm, and smiled again.

By the time the Count and his party had dismounted, entered the castle, and walked up the long, curving stairway to the audience chamber, Rudolph was waiting. Two soldiers were stationed on the right of his chair, two on the left. Count Meinhard and the Bishop of Basle came forward, and bowed to the Emperor.

"Your Majesty," Count Meinhard said. "We bring you the prisoner, Rabbi Meir ben Baruch of Rothenburg. Let him step forward."

R. Meir stepped away from the protection of his family. He faced the Emperor, eyeing him as coolly as he was being eyed.

"We meet again, Meir of Rothenburg," Rudolph said courteously.

R. Meir inclined his head in a small bow and answered. "We meet again, but I now at a disadvantage. Your Majesty well knows that I have never committed a crime. Therefore, Your Majesty, this arrest of my person is unjustified."

Rudolph leaned forward and looked at his prisoner keenly. "Rabbi, once you told me you had heard of my piety and my generosity. Perhaps you have heard also of my truthfulness. I shall tell you the truth. You have not

been arrested for any crime. You have been brought into my custody as an example."

The smoothness of R. Meir's face was broken by a frown. "An example, Your Majesty? An example of what?"

Rudolph leaned back, and spoke coldly. "An example to the Jews of Germany. Hundreds of them have been running away . . ."

"They run from slavery, Your Majesty."

"They run from their legal obligations," Rudolph said harshly. "And I have had you arrested to bring them to their senses. You will remain in custody until the Jews pay me the *servi camerae* tax."

"Never!" R. Meir exclaimed. "They will never pay that tax."

Rudolph leaned back suddenly, looking relaxed, smiling broadly. His voice was softer when he said, "Come, Rabbi, let us not be too hasty. Let us talk for a moment about something I have been thinking of for a long time. I know that you are the acknowledged leader of the Jews of Germany. I know that it is a great blessing for them to be led by so wise and so great a man as you."

R. Meir inclined his head in a slight bow, then said coldly, "The compliments serve no purpose, Your Majesty."

Rudolph smiled again. "Ah, but Rabbi, I say merely what everyone says. And I acknowledge what everyone knows. Meir of Rothenburg is the leader of the Jews. But . . ." He raised his hand as R. Meir seemed about to interrupt. "But you have never had the dignity of a proper title. I, now, I, Rudolph the First, Emperor of Germany, now proclaim you the Chief Rabbi of Germany!"

R. Meir's family behind him gasped in astonishment.

R. Meir smiled coolly at the Emperor. "It does indeed sound as though His Majesty has underestimated me. I do not believe I have ever been accused of possessing undue vanity. Titles mean nothing to me. And, Your Majesty," he paused and continued slowly to make his words impressive, "it is not within the province, if His Majesty will permit me to say so, of the Emperor to tell the Jews of Germany who their leader is to be."

Now the Bishop of Basle and Count Meinhard gasped.

A deep flush spread over Rudolph's face. He straightened up and it seemed as if he would lash out at R. Meir. But with an obvious attempt at controlling himself, he paused, and waited for his anger to subside. The red began to recede from his face and the glaze from his eyes. And when he spoke, his voice was as cool as R. Meir's, and his tones as measured.

"You will remain in custody until the Jews pay me the *servi camerae* tax."

"And I say, never!" R. Meir said coldly. "The Jews will never be enslaved. They will never pay that tax."

Rudolph leaned forward. "Then you will never be released!"

He turned now to R. Meir's bodyguard and spoke curtly. "You are ordered to leave the castle immediately.

If you are not gone within one-half hour, you will be arrested!"

"We will not go without our father!" Moses ben Simon said.

"No, no, my son," R. Meir turned to him. "Go. Please go, my sons. Do not add sorrow to my present grief. Go. Go in peace."

With a soldier to prod them forward, Solomon b. Isaac, Moses b. Simon, David, Joel, Judah and Meir Ha-Kohen left the castle.

R. Meir was escorted to a suite of rooms where he was put under heavy guard.

Meanwhile, his sons-in-law went into action. Moses b. Simon, his son Judah, and Meir Ha-Kohen remained at Wasserburg to find a house and to have it ready for the women and children when they arrived. Solomon b. Isaac and his sons David and Joel rode off to Cologne to seek out Hayyim b. Yehiel Jefetz Zahav, the brother of Asher b. Yehiel, R. Meir's former student. They hoped to get Hayyim to negotiate with the Emperor.

Hayyim b. Yehiel was shocked at R. Meir's arrest, and agreed immediately to seek the release of the great Teacher. He had had considerable experience in dealing with the nobles and the bishops.

Before going directly to Wasserburg to see the Emperor, he traveled to all the Jewish communities in Germany to inform them of what had happened to R. Meir. The Jews were stricken with grief at R. Meir's imprisonment. And terror! If the great Rabbi could be arrested, what would happen to them?

But their grief exceeded their fear. How could their beloved leader be permitted to remain a prisoner? Hayyim must make every effort to get him released. It was true that R. Meir's family could have raised the money needed for a ransom; but Hayyim felt it would be more effective if the money were to come from the Jewish community of Germany. And the Jews of Germany promised to pay any ransom Rudolph should demand of them. Armed with these pledges, Hayyim hurried to Wasserburg.

At Wasserburg the family was now settled in a large house near the castle. Meir Ha-Kohen went to the castle every day, bringing R. Meir his food and books and carrying messages from the family to him, and from him to the family. Meir Ha-Kohen was permitted to visit R. Meir as much as he wished. He went early every morning and stayed until late afternoon.

At first R. Meir was more concerned about his family than about himself. As the Emperor's prisoner, he was not molested in any way. The guards treated him respectfully and with deference. Every comfort was provided for him. He was allowed to have as many visitors as he wished and Meir Ha-Kohen and some of his other disciples came and studied with him. He was permitted to read, to do everything he desired—except leave the castle.

He expected that he would remain imprisoned for just a short time. Therefore he did not worry about himself at all, although he worried about his family. But Meir Ha-Kohen reassured him that all was well. The family was living in comfortable quarters, they lacked nothing for their ease or happiness, but, of course, they longed for his release.

"It will not be long, Meir," R. Meir said. "The Emperor will not have the audacity to keep me in prison, since he can charge me with no crime. Only one thing worries me, Meir—that Hayyim ben Yehiel is coming to deal with the Emperor. Hayyim will offer to ransom me. And that must not happen."

Meir Ha-Kohen looked at him in amazement. "But, my Master, how else can you be released if you are not ransomed? The Emperor wants money, and the Jews will ransom you."

"Ransom must not be paid," R. Meir said firmly. "Don't you realize, my son, what will happen if the Jews ransom me? Every month or so the Emperor will kidnap another prominent Jew and hold him for ransom. He will bleed us white and there will be no end to this. They must not ransom me!"

"But there is no other way to free you!" Meir Ha-Kohen said in despair. "Ransom is our only hope!"

R. Meir shook his head. "The Emperor has no legal right to hold me. When he finds out that the Jews refuse to pay a ransom, he will release me."

Meir Ha-Kohen, now deeply agitated, did not want to disturb his teacher further. They turned to some books he had brought, and talked about the legal code Meir Ha-Kohen had been working on. But Meir could not wait to get away. He wanted to see Rebecca.

When he reached the house in the late afternoon, he

took Rebecca out into the garden, where they could talk without being overheard and without interference. He repeated his conversation with her father to her.

"But he must be ransomed," she cried. "There is no other way. I must see him. I must talk to him. Meir, you must get me into the castle."

"Into the castle!" Meir laughed hollowly. "You know that's impossible. Women are not permitted to enter the castle. I cannot get you in, Rebecca. I cannot."

Rebecca interrupted him. "You are permitted to go in."

"Yes, I, and your husband, and your father's disciples —only men."

"Then I shall be a man!"

"You—a man! What foolishness are you talking, Rebecca?"

She paced up and down in excitement. "It is not foolishness, Meir. I shall dress as a man! And you will sneak me into the castle!"

"You cannot dress as a man! Rebecca! Calm down. Think. You know it is against Jewish law for a woman to dress as a man."

"Yes," she turned to him in excitement, her face blazing. "Yes, it's against the law. But it's against the law to keep my father in prison too. I must see him. I must talk to him. If I cannot go into the castle because I am a woman, then I shall go as a man!"

Nothing Meir said could swerve Rebecca once she decided to masquerade as a man to gain entrance to the castle. She swore him to secrecy. Even her husband must not know, or he would try to stop her because of the danger. If she were discovered it would go hard with her; she might even be put to death.

Meir at first refused to help her.

And then, in tears, she said, "Meir, we are both grown old now. We met first when we were fifteen years old. And now we are fifty. We have lived a lifetime in the same house. We have lived as brother and sister. You love my father as if he were your father. Once we quarrelled, you and I, because we both loved him so much. Now he is in trouble. And only you have the privilege of helping him. You go to him every day. You give him support with your presence, with your company. And I, I who have always adored him, I must stay on the outside and anguish in silence over his sorrow. Meir, I must see my father. You must help me."

Meir was defenseless against such a plea. He agreed.

The big problem was the disguise. What could she do to hide her long hair? How could she conceal her feminine walk? They puzzled over the problem for a long time, and then Rebecca exclaimed,

"A monk!"

Meir Ha-Kohen looked at her blankly. "A monk? What are you talking about?"

"I shall go as a monk," she said triumphantly. "It will be a perfect disguise."

And it was. The monk's robe completely hid her body and the hood concealed her hair.

Early one morning, just after dawn, when the light was not too clear, and when the guards were still somewhat sleepy, Meir Ha-Kohen approached the Castle at Wasserburg accompanied by a monk, Fra Bartholomew. The monk walked bent over, his face deep in his cowl, his hands lost in the folds of his sleeves. The guards barely noticed him.

Fra Bartholomew walked softly behind Meir Ha-Kohen across the stone floors of the castle, beyond the big corridor and up the stone steps, until they reached R. Meir's suite. Meir Ha-Kohen knocked on the door. R. Meir opened it, and stared in surprise at the monk.

"Greetings of peace, my Master," Meir Ha-Kohen said loudly, so that the guard standing nearby could hear. "This is Fra Bartholomew, who has arrived this morning from France. He wishes to speak to you on a matter of the church."

R. Meir frowned. He wondered what trick Meir Ha-Kohen was playing. Without ceremony, Meir Ha-Kohen gently nudged his teacher inside the room, and pushed the stooping monk after him. He closed the door quickly.

R. Meir started to say, "Meir, what . . ."

Fra Bartholomew raised his head, threw off his hood, and Rebecca, his daughter Rebecca, stood there laughing!

"Oh Father!" Her laughter turned to tears as she embraced him, thinking how worn and worried he looked, and how much thinner he had become in just these few months since she had seen him last in the inn on the highway to Gorz. "Oh Father. Forgive me. I had to see you. It is not Meir's fault. It is mine. But I had to see you. Father, Father, say you forgive me."

R. Meir smiled gently, as he stroked her hair. "My daughter, how can I not forgive you? What joy you bring me, to give me this sight of you."

Meir Ha-Kohen hovered in the background, still expecting R. Meir to turn on him and scold him for permitting Rebecca to disguise herself as a man and to endanger her life in this way. But R. Meir smiled at him over Rebecca's shoulder.

He led them to chairs near the window, and said, "If you had told me in advance what you planned to do, I would have expressly forbade it. But how can I be angry to see my own beloved daughter."

"Father!" Rebecca turned to him in great excitement. "Father, it was so easy! The guards didn't even question me. Father, you must take my clothes and disguise yourself as a monk, and escape, and I will stay here . . ."

R. Meir frowned at her. In a forbidding voice he said, "To be discovered? And be sent to your death? Have you lost all reason? No, Rebecca, I will not scold you for what you have done today. But I forbid you to do this again. You must promise me. Promise me now, with Meir Ha-Kohen as a witness, that you will never, never do this again."

Rebecca bowed her head. "But, Father, it was so easy, and if I could see you again . . ."

"Rebecca." It was Meir Ha-Kohen talking. "Rebecca, it was easy today. But if another time you were discovered, it would be death, Rebecca. Death for you . . . death for me . . . and death for your Father."

Rebecca turned to her father. "I promise, Father. I shall never do this again."

Then R. Meir relaxed, and asked many, many questions about each member of the family. He asked what Sarah said, how she looked, was Deborah well, and about the little children.

For a long time they talked about the family, and then finally Rebecca said,

"Father, Meir has told me that you refuse to be ransomed. Father, please, dear Father, you must listen to me. It is impossible to get you free without a ransom. You must permit it. It is the only way."

"Rebecca, please do not force me to go into the entire matter as I have already done with Meir. If it is impossible to release me in any other way, then I must remain in prison."

"But Father, it is such a waste! Such a waste of your life and your family's life."

"It is no waste, Rebecca. I read here. I study. See, I even continue my work here. Meir Ha-Kohen has been bringing me my correspondence and I am still writing my responsa, even from prison. So it is no waste. The only sorrow I have, Rebecca dear, is being separated from my family."

"Oh Father," Rebecca said. "How can you remain so strong?"

R. Meir smiled gently. "Dear Rebecca, let me tell you a story."

Rebecca permitted herself an inner smile. If she closed her eyes, she could imagine herself a child again, sitting in the garden at Rothenburg, listening to her beloved father telling stories to her and Deborah.

His voice, as she heard it now in the prison of the Castle of Wasserburg, was as strong and vibrant as it had ever been in their rose-garden.

"Once, my darling daughter," he said, "there was a great oak tree which was uprooted by the winds during a severe storm. It was carried down a river in which many reeds grew. The oak marvelled to see that such things, so light and frail, had withstood the storm which had uprooted so great and strong a tree as himself. And the reeds answered, 'Cease to wonder. You were overthrown by fighting against the storm, while we were saved by yielding and bending to the slightest breath that blows.' "

R. Meir's voice faded.

Rebecca smiled. "Yes, you have the patience of the reeds, but you also have the heart of the oak."

She pulled the monk's cowl over her head, preparing to leave. But the idea of walking freely out of the Castle, leaving her father behind, still a prisoner, overwhelmed her. She threw herself in his arms, and cried, "Oh, Father, why? Why must you be a martyr!"

R. Meir was silent for a moment. Then he spoke slowly. "Rebecca, my daughter, Meir, my son, I have no desire to be a martyr. But if this is what God means me to do, then I must accept my lot. I must accept it without tears. Listen to me, my children. If a man makes up his mind to be martyred, then, whatever they will do to him . . . whether it is stoning or beating or burning, nothing will hurt him.

"If I must remain in prison the rest of my life, I accept my lot."

16

Ensisheim

Hayyim b. Yehiel Jefetz
Zahav came to Wasserburg and received an immediate
audience with the Emperor. Rudolph was even more
anxious for this meeting than Hayyim. Every day that R.
Meir remained imprisoned delayed the yielding of the
Jews to the new taxation.

Hayyim was received in the audience chamber of
Wasserburg Castle. After the social formalities of talk
had been indulged in, Hayyim said,

"And my revered friend and teacher, Rabbi Meir,
Your Majesty, how is his health?"

"Rest on that score, sir. Rabbi Meir is in good health.
We have treated him kindly and well. He has not lacked
for comforts. Yes, yes, you will find him well."

"I am happy to hear that, Your Majesty. And now, if

Your Majesty permits, perhaps we may talk about the ransom price for Rabbi Meir."

Rudolph glared at Hayyim. "There is to be no talk of ransom money, now or later. If you have come here to ransom the Rabbi, then you waste your time and mine. The Rabbi will be released, but only when the sum of money due is paid to me as taxes, as legal taxes, and openly acknowledged as such!"

"Your Majesty, that is impossible," protested Hayyim. "The Jews will not consent to pay the *servi camerae* tax which you are trying to enforce. They are willing to pay a ransom, and a good ransom, for Rabbi Meir, but it must be understood that it is *special* ransom-money, and *not* tax money."

"No!" shouted the Emperor, pounding the arm of the chair. "A thousand times no! That money will be paid to me as regular taxes . . . or the Rabbi will stay in prison until he dies."

Hayyim turned pale. "Oh no, Your Majesty . . ."

"Oh yes," Rudolph countered. "I have the ring-leader of this rebellion and I mean to keep him. I have repeatedly demanded the tax from the Jews. They have refused to pay because Rabbi Meir tells them to refuse. So he will remain my prisoner until the Jews pay this *tax*. I will not accept a ransom. I accept only an honest tax."

Hayyim fell silent. There was no use continuing to say "no" to the Emperor's "yes."

"Well?" the Emperor demanded impatiently.

"Your Majesty," Hayyim said. "The Jews are ready and willing to pay you 20,000 pounds as ransom-money for Rabbi Meir."

The Emperor rose. "Perhaps you are weary from travel, and you are too tired to hear me well. I say 'tax' and you persist in saying 'ransom.' The correct word, my dear Hayyim ben Yehiel, is *TAX*. Go and rest. When you are thinking clearly again, when you understand that 'tax' is not 'ransom,' you will return to me, and we shall settle this matter."

The Emperor turned his back on him in dismissal.

But Hayyim did not leave. "Your Majesty, may I have permission to visit Rabbi Meir?"

The Emperor motioned to the soldier on guard at the door. "Escort this man to the prisoner's quarters."

The soldier led Hayyim to R. Meir's suite. The two men were happy to see each other, but Hayyim came straight to the point. He was so disturbed by his conversation with the Emperor that he just blurted it out.

"Dear Rabbi, we have the money, 20,000 pounds. We believe the Emperor is willing to accept 20,000 pounds. But he insists that it must be in the form of taxation, and we are trying to pay it as a ransom."

R. Meir burst into angry words, surprising Hayyim. The Rabbi was known to have a quick and a sharp temper, but he had never before seen it evidenced. R. Meir spoke bitterly.

"The church and the kings of Europe are money-mad. They leave the Jews nothing to trade in but money and second-hand goods—new gold or old iron—and then they revile us as usurers. Yes, we trade in money, because we are forced to. But we do not love money. *They* love money. They are money-mad . . . money is their ruling passion . . . it is all they live for. They have only one desire in life, to separate the Jew from his money. Do you think they wish to convert us to Christianity? Oh no! How then could they keep on taxing us illegally? All they want is to tear us to bits, piece by piece, into chunks of money to satisfy their greedy throats. I say NO! We will pay the Emperor nothing! Nothing, do you hear!"

"But Rabbi Meir," Hayyim said. "If we pay nothing you will languish here in prison."

"Listen to me, Hayyim. This Emperor wants to enslave the Jews. If we obey him and pay these taxes, we shall be handing over our lives to him. I say no, Hayyim, no. We will not be enslaved. The Jew was enslaved only once in his life, when he lived in Egypt. He will never be enslaved again. Do you hear me, Hayyim? We will never consent to be enslaved again. If you pay Rudolph one penny now, you will be committing the Jews to degrading servitude. I will not permit it! You will not force me to permit it. I will not have you buy my freedom and thus enslave my people."

"But if we get the Emperor to accept it as a ransom. . . ."

"He will never accept it as a ransom. Do not be deceived, Hayyim. The Emperor means to enforce the *servi camerae* decree. I will not permit it. You will return to him. You will say to him, NO!"

"But, Rabbi, Rabbi." Hayyim was almost weeping. "He may kill you."

"Then he will kill me," R. Meir said calmly. "My life is almost over. I am seventy-one years old. How much longer can I hope to live . . ."

"Your father lived much longer," Hayyim wailed.

R. Meir shrugged. "I have had a long life and a good life and if I must die, I will die, but I will never permit the Jews to be enslaved just so that I may live another year or two. No, Hayyim, that is my final word. Go and give the Emperor my message."

Hayyim had no chance for further argument. R. Meir unceremoniously showed him the door. He returned to the audience chamber, to speak to the Emperor again.

"Sire, please listen to me." Now Hayyim was begging the Emperor. "Please accept the 20,000 pounds as ransom-money. Rabbi Meir refuses to let me pay any money at all, but if you will accept the ransom . . ."

Rudolph shouted at Hayyim. "I say no! *No* to ransom-money. I will accept 20,000 pounds, but as *Kammer-knechte* money . . ."

"And that is only the beginning?" Hayyim asked despairingly.

Rudolph shrugged. "Of course. It is only the beginning. However, unless you pay me 20,000 pounds, for a start, as *Kammerknechte* money, the Rabbi remains imprisoned."

There the matter stood. Hayyim entreated with R. Meir three more times, and each time R. Meir forbade him to pay *Kammerknechte* money. Three times Hayyim returned to the Emperor and offered the 20,000 pounds as ransom-money, and each time the Emperor refused to accept it as a ransom.

Hayyim went to R. Meir's family and begged them to

intercede with the Rabbi. To everyone who pleaded with him, R. Meir gave the same answer.

"The Jews will not be enslaved to save my life. If I die as a martyr for my people, I die. I will not have them enslaved."

Once more Hayyim b. Yehiel Jefetz Zahav went to the Emperor, Rudolph I of Hapsburg. And to the Emperor, Hayyim said, "Your Majesty. I have failed."

Rudolph looked hard at Hayyim, then turned on his heel and strode out of the room.

Hayyim was left with the unpleasant task of returning to the family of R. Meir to tell them of his failure.

Sarah, grown old and feeble under the troubles which had come to them, could only weep. Deborah stayed at her side to comfort her.

It was Rebecca who asked. "What will happen now?"

No one knew the answer. Silence fell. The family grieved.

There was activity at the Castle, however. During the night, while the city slept, while R. Meir's family tossed in restless sleep, the Emperor spirited R. Meir away from the Castle.

Early the next morning, when Meir Ha-Kohen came as usual to see his teacher, the guard informed him brusquely, "They are gone."

"Gone? Gone where?"

The guard turned sharply around and marched away. Meir Ha-Kohen ran from guard to guard, but no one would tell him where they had taken R. Meir, or what had happened to him.

"They have killed him!" Deborah cried.

"No, no," Rebecca insisted. "Then there would be no need for secrecy. They have taken him elsewhere. We shall find out! We must find out!"

But it took almost a month, and then finally, one of the guards at the Castle, feeling sorry for Meir Ha-Kohen, uttered one word: "Ensisheim."

"Ensisheim!" Rebecca exclaimed when Meir rushed home to tell the family. "Where is Ensisheim?"

"It is in the upper Alsace," Meir said. "There is an old fortress there. R. Meir must be in that fortress."

Meir Ha-Kohen and Judah b. Moses, Deborah's son, left immediately for Alsace, leaving the family to follow more slowly. By the time the family reached Ensisheim, Judah had already found a house for the family and Meir Ha-Kohen had re-established contact with R. Meir.

Life at Ensisheim continued as it had at Wasserburg. Meir Ha-Kohen and R. Meir's students were permitted to visit him constantly. R. Meir was able to continue with his studies. Scholars all over the world soon discovered that he was incarcerated in the fortress at Ensisheim, and they began to send him letters containing questions on Jewish law. He continued to write his responsa, the answers to these questions. Once more, R. Meir's life and the life of his family fell into a pattern from which there could be no change.

R. Meir remained firm in his decision that he would remain in prison, rather than permit the Jews to be enslaved with the paying of the *Kammerknechte* money. The Emperor Rudolph remained firm in his resolve that the Rabbi would stay in prison unless the *servi camerae* tax were paid.

The two old men remained stubborn. Neither one could be budged.

"He will stay in prison all his life," Rudolph said.

"I shall remain in prison until I die," R. Meir said.

The first one who lost courage was Sarah. She had suffered keenly over her husband's imprisonment. She knew the reasons for his refusal to be ransomed, she understood, she approved, but his imprisonment broke her heart. On the day of the first anniversary of R. Meir's arrest, Sarah died.

Meir Ha-Kohen brought the sad news to R. Meir. After he had wept, and Meir Ha-Kohen had tried to comfort him, R. Meir said, "Meir, my son, tell Deborah to plant a myrtle tree on the grave of my beloved. Deborah will remember the story I once told her. When Adam was banished from Eden, he was allowed to take away with him one memento. He plucked a leaf off the myrtle tree, and now it has become a symbol of the hope for Paradise and Eternal Life. Plant a myrtle tree on Sarah's grave."

The old man broke into soft weeping and Meir Ha-Kohen wept with him. After a while, their weeping ended, as they sat with dry eyes and drained hearts, Meir Ha-Kohen said,

"Now, Rabbi, now is the time to permit yourself to be released, for the sake of Sarah's memory. She grieved too much. She sorrowed over your fate. For the sake of Sarah's memory, let them pay the taxes to Rudolph."

R. Meir sighed and shook his head. "No, Meir, no. It would be a betrayal of her. She knew I acted in the only way I could. To buy my freedom at the cost of the slavery of my people—no, the cost is too great. The reward is too small. The cost outweighs the reward."

Meir burst out bitterly. "You are stubborn, Rabbi."

His mouth fell open and he remained frozen for a moment in shock, that he had spoken so to his Teacher! He found his voice and stammered, "Forgive me, my Teacher, forgive . . ."

R. Meir, even in his grief, found a smile for his friend.

"But you are right, Meir. I am stubborn. A Jew must be stubborn, to live. He must stubbornly remind the world that justice must prevail, that mercy must endure, that truth must rise and rise and never fall to earth. That is our task."

"Our task," Meir Ha-Kohen said without spirit. "We have failed in our task."

"No, no, Meir, never say that," said R. Meir. "The task of the Jew is the purpose of his entire existence. There is more to life than seeking happiness for one's self. The Jew must seek to destroy idolatry—the undue love of money, the ruin of souls through injustice, the hatred, the cruelty, the wars—all these idolatries must be destroyed, Meir. The Jew must bring the world to the pure worship of God."

"Even if we are crushed in the process?"

"We will not be crushed, Meir. Listen to this story."

Meir Ha-Kohen bit his lips to keep from crying out, "No, no, Master, now is not the time for stories." But he looked into the old man's serene eyes and thought, yes, anything that helps him forget his grief is good. So he said softly,

"What is the story, my Teacher?"

R. Meir spoke as softly. "When the Temple was destroyed by Nebuchadnezzar, God found Abraham in the ruins of the Temple. He was praying. And God said, 'What doth My beloved in My house?' And Abraham said, 'I am here, O Lord, because of my children.' And God said, 'Your children have sinned.' And Abraham said, 'But, O Lord, God forbid that there should be no salvation for them.' Whereupon a Heavenly Voice echoed:- 'The Lord called Thy people's name a "green olive-tree," whose product comes after pressure and crushing. Even so will Israel's salvation come after its suffering.' "

Meir Ha-Kohen bent his head. He whispered, "And I dare to call you stubborn."

R. Meir said softly, "The Jew must be stubborn, to live."

He paused. Then he whispered, "Farewell, Sarah. Farewell, my beloved wife."

17

The Flame of Life

EARLY on the morning of January first, in the year 1288, Hayyim b. Yehiel burst into the family house in Ensisheim.

"Rebecca," he shouted. "Deborah. Solomon. Moses. I have news! I have news!"

The family came running from every corner of the house.

"Hayyim, where have you come from?"

"Hayyim, it is so long since we've seen you."

"Hayyim, what is the news? What is it?"

It was Rebecca's voice which shouted out over the others.

"Quiet, everyone, please. Please." As every voice hushed, she clutched Hayyim's arm. "Oh, we had given up hope completely, Hayyim. What news could you possibly bring?"

"Hope!" shouted Hayyim. "I bring the message of hope! I have been to Rome. I have seen the Pope!"

"The Pope!"

"Nicholas IV!"

"You have seen the Pope?"

"I have seen the Pope. Pope Nicholas IV is going to intercede for Rabbi Meir. He is going to request the Emperor Rudolph to release Rabbi Meir!"

"Release!"

"The Pope!"

"God bless the Pope!"

Meir Ha-Kohen rushed away from the family, out of the house, to hurry to the fortress to bring the news to R. Meir.

"The Pope intercedes for you!"

"The Pope!"

For four days the family was in a frenzy of excitement. Pope Nicholas IV has interceded. He has requested the Emperor to release the Rabbi.

The Lord is good.

The Lord is good.

On the morning of the fifth day, Hayyim walked slowly into the house of the family. Rebecca looked at his waxen face. She whispered, "Hayyim? It is lost?"

Hayyim nodded. He turned his back on her, and his voice came thick and mumbled. "The Emperor refuses to listen to the plea of the Pope."

Now with lagging steps, Meir Ha-Kohen went to the fortress to bring R. Meir the ashes of hope.

R. Meir put his hand on Meir's shoulder, and smiled

faintly. He even shook him a little. "Come, Meir," he teased. "It is not the end of the world. The Pope asked. The Emperor refused. It is God's will. We accept the will of the Lord."

By now Meir Ha-Kohen felt crushed by a vast feeling of injustice. He, more than anyone else, had seen what the years of imprisonment had done to his great Teacher.

Not to his spirit. Not to his mind. His spirit was still courageous and his mind was still keen, alert, sharp.

But his poor body had become thin and frail and bent. His face was grey and sallow from lack of sunlight and fresh air. His hands trembled a trifle, and lines of discouragement had furrowed his forehead. But his eyes were still clear and bright, and his voice rang out now confidently:

"It is God's will!"

"But where is the justice?" Meir Ha-Kohen almost shouted.

"Ah, justice." R. Meir smiled. "Justice is here, Meir, here, there and everywhere in the world. God's justice is always at work. Often we do not see it, because we imagine that every act of every individual should show the effect of justice immediately. But God's ways are immense and mysterious. We may not always know His reasons, but *He* knows. Sometimes it takes years and generations for justice to triumph. But finally it does, Meir! Always!"

"How can you speak so confidently, you who are the victim of such a cruel injustice?" Meir asked.

"I more than you, Meir," R. Meir said, "just because I am the victim of injustice. God's ways are just. I trust in the Lord."

Meir Ha-Kohen could only bow his head. Then he murmured, "But your suffering . . . your loneliness . . ."

"My suffering." R. Meir smiled, looking out over Meir Ha-Kohen's head through the windows, up into the sky. "Our sorrow," he said, "our suffering, our loneliness become the altar upon which, purified by suffering, we worship God. Listen, Meir, to the words of our poet, to the words of Judah the Saint:-

> " 'From the broken fragments of my heart
> I will build an altar unto Thee.' "

And now, with no hope of release, R. Meir settled back into his routine of life, uncomplaining, cheerful, working hard. During all the years that followed, he never ceased to work.

In the year 1292 hopes for the release of R. Meir awakened again in the hearts of the family. In this year the Emperor, Rudolph the First of Hapsburg, died.

"I do not rejoice over his death," Rebecca said defensively to Deborah when they heard the news. "But now that that stubborn old man is gone, surely we shall be able to convince the new Emperor to release our dear Father from his prison."

"Who is to be the new Emperor?" Deborah asked in a dull voice. She did not share Rebecca's high hope.

It was as their mother had seen years before when they were little girls—Rebecca would always fly on the wings of hope and laughter; Deborah would always go more slowly, feeling sorrow more quickly and keenly.

No one knew who the new Emperor would be, and they waited anxiously to hear. Meanwhile, Meir Ha-Kohen had gone to the fortress to tell R. Meir of Rudolph's death.

R. Meir sighed. "May his soul rest in peace."

Meir Ha-Kohen laughed lightly. "Though he was your enemy, my Master?"

R. Meir smiled. "The Talmud teaches us that we must comfort Gentiles when they mourn and, if need be, we must bury their dead as we do the dead of our own people. I know he was my enemy, Meir, and that his whole life was motivated by greed. But now, in the grave, may he find peace for his troubled spirit. Perhaps now he has learned something Alexander the Great learned early in his brief career."

Meir Ha-Kohen smiled as he felt a story coming on. But his heart was so lightened by the possibility of R. Meir's release that he wanted to help his old Teacher enjoy the moment.

"A story, Rabbi?" he teased.

R. Meir's eyes twinkled. "Yes, Meir, a story.

"Once Alexander the Great traveled through the Land of Darkness and came to the entrance of Paradise. When he wished to enter, he was refused permission. In his arrogance, he said, 'If you refuse me admittance, then give me a worthy gift, for I am a great Emperor.' The guardian went away and returned, carrying a pair of scales and a little ball. He said to Alexander, 'On one side of the scales, place everything you possess.' And so onto the scale Alexander put everything, his wealth, his lands, his treasures, his friends, his life, his hope, his youth. The little ball was placed on the other side of the scale. And to his amazement, the little ball outweighed them all. And he asked, 'What is this little ball?' And he was told, 'It is an eyeball, a greedy eyeball.' 'Can nothing conquer it?' Alexander asked. And he was told, 'Yes, a small thing, a handful of dust. A handful of dust is all that it takes to bury a man. The handful of dust will conquer the greedy eye.' "

As the story concluded, R. Meir sighed and said, "Yes, Meir, a handful of dust is all that is needed to bury a man. Nothing else but a handful of dust can satisfy greed. While he lived, Rudolph could never be satisfied. Now he is dead. His hopes, his dreams, his greedy desires are dead with him. Let him be in peace, Meir."

One greedy Emperor was laid to rest, and another rose to take his place. Adolph, of the House of Nassau, became Emperor. The hopes of R. Meir and his family were dashed almost immediately.

Adolph had not the grace of Rudolph, nor his courtesy. His answer to the request that Rabbi Meir ben Baruch of Rothenburg be released was given curtly and harshly:

"No! No *Kammerknechte* money, no release."

Once more the family tried to persuade the old Rabbi to give in and to permit the tax to be paid so that he might be freed. His answer was more courteous than that of Adolph of Nassau, but just as firm.

"No, my children, no. It is God's will."

Hope and the destruction of hope had alternated throughout the years. And now there was no more hope. But Meir ben Baruch remained cheerful, courageous, industrious. He found pleasure in his life, and his life was study and work.

On the morning of May 2, in the year 1293, R. Meir awoke at sunrise. He looked through the window to see the sun, a red ball of fire. His head felt heavy and pains tore through his chest.

"I am sick," he said. "And I am dying."

He lay down again on his bed, facing the window to see the flaming sunrise. And for a moment, the red ball of the sun turned into the flames of the fire in Paris in 1242 when the mobs burned the Talmud.

"From the burning Talmud in Paris to a flaming sunrise in Ensisheim," he murmured. "That is the circle of my life."

In that circle there had lived a great man. He was great in his faith, which gave him the courage to face life and its dangers. He was great in his achievements, which gave help and assistance to his brethren in many lands. He was great as a teacher, and from his consecrated work had come inspiration to many scholars, and many generations. The spirit of learning had burned brightly in R. Meir's heart and in its glowing words he had found renewed life and renewed hope. The Talmud which he had seen in flames in Paris had been a pillar of fire to guide his people through years of darkness.

And now the circle was closing.

To his lips came the poem he had written in Paris at the burning of the Talmuds, and he murmured,

> "My heart shall be uplifted on the day
>   Thy Rock shall be Thy light,
> When He shall make thy gloom to pass away,
>   Thy darkness bright."

Rabbi Meir smiled. He put his head back on the pillow.

He sighed, and then he died.

The flame of the life of Rabbi Meir ben Baruch whispered away in the breeze of eternity.

Epilogue

FOR FOURTEEN years after
the death of R. Meir of Rothenburg, his body remained
imprisoned in the fortress of Ensisheim. The Emperor
Adolph of the House of Nassau was deposed in the year
1298. Albert, Rudolph's son, became Emperor.

But he was no more willing to release the body of the
martyred Rabbi than his father had been to release the
living man. And still R. Meir's body was held prisoner.

In 1308, the Emperor Albert was assassinated, and
Henry, the Count of Luxembourg, became the Emperor.
He was persuaded to release R. Meir's body. Alexander
b. Solomon Wimpfen of Frankfort-on-the-Main paid
over a large sum of money as ransom for the release of
R. Meir's body. For that noble deed he asked only one
reward: that when he should die, he would be buried
next to the Rabbi.

Alexander b. Solomon Wimpfen brought R. Meir's

body to the city of Worms, where he had been born, and buried him next to his father, Baruch b. Isaac. When Alexander died he was buried next to Rabbi Meir ben Baruch of Rothenburg.

COVENANT BOOKS

*Stories of Jewish men and women to inspire and instruct
young people*

1. SILVERSMITH OF OLD NEW YORK:
   MYER MYERS
   by William Wise

2. BORDER HAWK: AUGUST BONDI
   by Lloyd Alexander

3. THE WORLD OF JO DAVIDSON
   by Lois Harris Kuhn

4. JUBAL AND THE PROPHET
   by Frieda Clark Hyman

5. THE UNCOMMON SOLDIER
   by Robert D. Abrahams

6. THE VOICE OF LIBERTY
   by Eva Merriam

7. KEYS TO A MAGIC DOOR
   by Silvia Rothchild

8. ABOAB, FIRST RABBI OF THE AMERICAS
   by Emily Hahn

9. NORTHWEST PIONEER
   by Alfred Apsler

10. ALBERT EINSTEIN
    by William Wise

11. BUILDERS OF JERUSALEM
    by Frieda Clark Hyman

12. FLAGSHIP HOPE: AARON LOPEZ
    by Lloyd Alexander

13. SCHOLAR-FIGHTER: SAADIA GAON
    by L. M. Klapperman